FIRSTplace
FOR HEALTH

MYplace

FOR BIBLE STUDY

Published by First Place for Health
Galveston, Texas, USA
www.firstplaceforhealth.com
Printed in the USA

ISBN: 978-1-942425-44-1

CONTENTS

MY PLACE FOR BIBLE STUDY

God's Purpose for You

FOREWORD

I was introduced to First Place for Health in 1993 by my mother-in-law, who had great concern for the welfare of her grandchildren. I was overweight and overwrought! God used that first Bible study to start me on my journey to health, wellness, and a life of balance.

Our desire at First Place for Health is for you to begin that same journey. We want you to experience the freedom that comes from an intimate relationship with Jesus Christ and witness His love for you through reading your Bible and through prayer. To this end, we have designed each day's study (which will take about fifteen to twenty minutes to complete) to help you discover the deep truths of the Bible. Also included is a weekly Bible memory verse to help you hide God's Word in your heart. As you start focusing on these truths, God will begin a great work in you.

At the beginning of Jesus' ministry, when He was teaching from the book of Isaiah, He said to the people, "The Spirit of the Lord is on me, because he has anointed me to preach good news to the poor. He has sent me to proclaim freedom for the prisoners and recovery of sight for the blind, to release the oppressed, to proclaim the year of the Lord's favor" (Luke 4:18–19). Jesus came to set us free—whether that is from the chains of compulsivity, addiction, gluttony, overeating, under eating, or just plain unbelief. It is our prayer that He will bring freedom to your heart so you may experience abundant life.

God bless you as you begin this journey toward a life of liberty.

Vicki Heath, First Place for Health National Director

ABOUT THE AUTHOR

Lucinda Secrest McDowell, M.T.S., is a storyteller and seasoned mentor who engages both heart and mind while "Helping You Choose a Life of Serenity & Strength." A graduate of Gordon-Conwell Theological Seminary and Furman University, McDowell is the author of 15 books and contributing author to 36+ books. Her award-winning books include *Soul Strong, Life-Giving Choices, Dwelling Places,* and *Ordinary Graces.*

Lucinda, a member of the Redbud Writers Guild and AWSA, received Mt. Hermon Writer of the Year award and guest blogs monthly for The Write Conversation. In addition to writing three First Place for Health Bible Studies, she serves on the FP4H Advisory Council, is active in her weekly FP4H author Bible study, and helps coordinate one of the annual FP4H Wellness Weeks. Whether coaching writers and speakers, pouring into young mamas, or leading a restorative day of prayer, she is energized by investing in people of all ages. As a communications teacher, she has served on the faculty of several writers conferences and co-directs the annual spiritual retreat reNEW – retreat for New England Writing & Speaking. Known for her ability to convey deep truth in practical and winsome ways, McDowell shares words from "Sunnyside" cottage in New England and blogs weekly at www.LucindaSecrestMcDowell.com Contact her through LucindaSMcDowell@gmail.com

ABOUT THE CONTRIBUTOR

Lisa Lewis, who provided the menus and recipes in this study, is the author of *Healthy Happy Cooking*. Lisa's cooking skills have been a part of First Place for Health wellness weeks and other events for many years. She provided recipes for seventeen of the First Place for Health Bible studies and is a contributing author in *Better Together* and *Healthy Holiday Living*. She partners with community networks, including the Real Food Project, to bring healthy cooking classes to underserved areas. She is dedicated to bringing people together around the dinner table with healthy, delicious meals that are easy to prepare. Lisa lives in Galveston and is married to John. They have three children: Tal, Hunter, and Harper. Visit www.healthyhappycook.com for more delicious inspiration.

INTRODUCTION

First Place for Health is a Christ-centered health program that emphasizes balance in the physical, mental, emotional, and spiritual areas of life. The First Place for Health program is meant to be a daily process. As we learn to keep Christ first in our lives, we will find that He is the One who satisfies our hunger and our every need.

This Bible study is designed to be used in conjunction with the First Place for Health program but can be beneficial for anyone interested in obtaining a balanced lifestyle. The Bible study has been created in a seven-day format, with the last two days reserved for reflection on the material studied. Keep in mind that the ultimate goal of studying the Bible is not only for knowledge but also for application and a changed life. Don't feel anxious if you can't seem to find the correct answer. Many times, the Word will speak differently to different people, depending on where they are in their walk with God and the season of life they are experiencing. Be prepared to discuss with your fellow First Place for Health members what you learned that week through your study.

There are some additional components included with this study that will be helpful as you pursue the goal of giving Christ first place in every area of your life:

○ **Leader Discussion Guide:** This discussion guide is provided to help the First Place for Health leader guide a group through this Bible study. It includes ideas for facilitating a First Place for Health class discussion for each week of the Bible study.

○ **Jump Start Recipes:** There are seven days of recipes--breakfast, lunch and dinner-- to get you started.

○ **Steps for Spiritual Growth:** This section will provide you with some basic tips for how to memorize Scripture and make it a part of your life, establish a quiet time with God each day, and share your faith with others..

○ **First Place for Health Member Survey:** Fill this out and bring it to your first meeting. This information will help your leader know your interests and talents.

○ **Personal Weight and Measurement Record:** Use this form to keep a record of your weight loss. Record any loss or gain on the chart after the weigh-in at each week's meeting.

○ **Weekly Prayer Partner Forms:** Fill out this form before class and place it into a basket during the class meeting. After class, you will draw out a prayer request form, and this will be your prayer partner for the week. Try to call or email the person sometime before the next class meeting to encourage that person.

○ **100-Mile Club:** A worthy goal we encourage is for you to complete 100 miles of exercise during your twelve weeks in First Place for Health. There are many activities listed on pages 265-266 that count toward your goal of 100 miles and a handy tracker to track your miles.

○ **Live It Trackers:** Your Live It Tracker is to be completed at home and turned in to your leader at your weekly First Place for Health meeting. The Tracker is designed to help you practice mindfulness and stay accountable with regard to your eating and exercise habits.

WEEK ONE: DISCOVER PURPOSE

SCRIPTURE MEMORY VERSE
But I have raised you up for this very purpose, that I might show you my power and that my name might be proclaimed in all the earth. Exodus 9:16 NIV

"What is your Why?" asked the podcast host as she interviewed me about my writing and speaking. What a perfect question for this season of life. So many of us are questioning not only what we spend our lives doing, but perhaps even more importantly *why.*"

As I considered this question, it became more and more apparent to me how strategic it is for each of us to determine God's purpose for our lives. What is our *telos* – the aim, the macro reason and goal -- our life's ultimate purpose? What inspires *you* to get out of bed each morning and move forward in purpose and power?

This word "inspire" derives from the Latin meaning "to breath life into." You may recall several biblical examples of our Creator doing this very thing:

- Genesis 2:7 Then the Lord God formed a man from the dust of the ground and breathed into his nostrils the breath of life and the man became a living being.
- Job 33:4 The Spirit of God has made me; the breath of the Almighty gives me life.

Did you know that God wants to breath new life into you today? At a critical turning point in his own life, Moses received a fresh breath from God who reminded him that there was both a plan and a purpose in the midst of a complicated life.

In this week's memory verse, Exodus 9:16, what two purposes did God have as he raised up Moses and called him forth?
1. _____
2. _____

What a great reminder that God wants us to live daily through His divine power and to spread the glory of His name far and wide. But sadly, I have not always done this. Instead of living with power, too often I have failed to maintain balance – physical, spiritual, mental, and emotional. You too?

In my own life, I have struggled with roller-coaster weight—reaching one goal only to slide back into old habits. At times I often wondered if it was even possible to maintain a healthy life. But during these next weeks, through God's Purpose for You, I will be sharing how to make positive changes based on God's power and plan—changes that will enable you to be transformed in each area of health: physical, spiritual, mental, and emotional.

Perhaps you have not yet experienced God at work in your life, and you long to learn how to invite Him in. God created us inside and out and desires us to keep soul and body in balance. If either is ignored, the other part suffers. Whether you have already begun getting your life in balance or are just starting out, *God's Purpose for You* will be a guide to what God's Word has to say about the process.

When I begin a journey, I remind myself enthusiastically, *"I'm not what I wanna be; I'm not what I'm gonna be . . . but praise God Almighty, I'm not what I was!"* May I also remind you that you are not alone but traveling with fellow seekers. You may know the other members of your group well or you may be just getting acquainted. Whatever the case, remember that even though you come with differing agendas and backgrounds, you meet on level ground at the foot of the cross. Jesus will meet each of you where you are and ask, *"Do you want to get well?"* Your response may just change your life forever.

As we search for God's purpose, the first step is to take stock of where we are. The second step is to ask God to show us where He wants us to be, and how to get there. This is done through prayer and the study of God's Word. As we align our desires with His, committing to do what is necessary to achieve our goals, He promises to give us divine power to overcome any obstacles in our path. As you grow in strength and daily disciplines, you will be able to stand firm against the enemy of your soul, the one who is trying to keep you down and defeated, discouraged, and depressed. Grasping tightly to God's truth and listening to His guiding voice, you can go forward with the assurance that your life doesn't have to be a roller coaster of highs and lows—you can live in balance and encourage others to do the same!

—— DAY 1: BODY AND SOUL

Lord, give me a new vision of the balanced life You have for me, which will come as I follow Your will and Your way, Help me to experience the blessing of a strong body and soul. In Christ's name, Amen.

"Dear friend, I hope all is well with you, and that you are as healthy in body as you are strong in spirit." 3 John 1.2 NIV

John, Jesus' dearest friend, spent his later years urging followers of the Way to live with purpose. In this verse he is communicating that both physical health and spiritual strength are important for all to be well. Why is this such a perennial struggle? As I look back at my life, there were seasons where I focused almost exclusively on my outer appearance to the neglect of my inner life. But then, there were also seasons where I poured into soul care and holy living whilst completely ignoring the upkeep of my physical body. Neither was healthy, and neither was godly.

Can you identify struggles in both of these areas?
1. To be healthy in body _____
2. To be strong in spirit _____

Jesus knew that sometimes we battle within ourselves. What does he remind us in Matthew 26:41?

My spirit is _____, but my flesh is _____so I am reminded to _____ and _____.

Some of us struggle for a lifetime to finally embrace God's view of our bodies, instead believing the lies of the culture. In my own journey, I've experienced life as a chubby child, a slender teen, and a morbidly obese adult. At one point after too much yo-yo dieting, I gave up in exasperation and turned to food to meet my emotional needs. I remained in that miserable rut for years.

My sin was not being overweight; my sin was turning to another substance (food) to meet needs that only God can meet. In my disobedience, I was not a good steward of all He had entrusted to me. Over time food had become more than sustenance – food brought comfort, love, security, companionship, distraction, and a way to numb myself so I wouldn't have to face the real issues that needed spiritual transformation. Our bodies and souls are entwined. In desperation and defeat, I eventually cried out to God, *"I don't want to live this way anymore! Whatever it takes, I am willing to do the hard work of change – from the inside out."* And He met me where I was and has never left my side in this struggle. My Creator knows I must begin with spiritual transformation inside in order to make lasting physical changes.

How does the Spirit confirm God's purpose in our lives? Romans 8.16?

_____

_____

_____

I desperately wanted to be freed from being consumed with my weight. I desired a healthy perspective – intentional but not preoccupied. I wanted food to be just food, to take its place of importance, but not greater. When I realized I was scheduling my life around food (instead of food around my life) I knew I was in trouble.

The First Place for Health lifestyle offers hope through the wisdom of seeking God first to restore the balance God ordered for us – spiritual, physical, mental and emotional. "Love the Lord your God with all your heart and with all your soul and with all your mind and with all your strength." Mark 12:30 NIV

Write down how each of these verses encourage a healthy view of your body and spirit?
Ephesians 2:10 _____
1 Timothy 4:8 _____
Psalm 139:14 _____
1 Samuel 16:7b _____
Genesis 1:27 _____

I love how Caleb in the Old Testament lived with balance of body and spirit. I'm especially encouraged at how he thrived between the ages of forty and eighty-five! Because Caleb was born while the nation of Israel was enslaved in Egypt, he most probably spent the first forty years of his life in grueling slave labor until the Lord miraculously freed his people to journey through the Red Sea and eventually into the promised land. Of the thousands of men, Caleb stood out to Moses as Judah's leader when it was time to send one from each tribe to spy out the land. What were these men asked to do? Numbers 13:17-20

_____

_____

_____

When the men returned, they described Canaan as a land flowing with milk and honey, but heavily guarded by frightening giants – the Anaks, What was Caleb's report to Moses and Aaron? Numbers 13:30?

_____
_____
_____

How did their traveling companions respond? Numbers 13:31-33?

_____
_____
_____

Only Joshua, son of Nun, and Caleb, son of Jephunneh, were brave enough to argue for going forward into Canaan. What was their logic? Numbers 14:6-9

_____
_____
_____

As you begin this new study, *God's Purpose for You* write down where you need to hear Caleb's words in your own life? Numbers 14:9

"The Lord is with us."_____
"Do not be afraid of them."_____

What do we learn about Caleb as a man from the Lord's words in Numbers 14:24?

_____
_____
_____

Sadly, the cautious majority prevailed, and the Israelites wandered in the desert for forty more years! After Moses died and Joshua was set to lead the Israelites across the Jordan River into the Promised Land, Caleb was still by his side. I believe Caleb stayed healthy in both body and spirit because he had deep faith in God and deep passion to help lead his people onward to their God-given destiny. He describes it in his own words here:

"Now then, just as the LORD promised, he has kept me alive for forty-five years since the time he said this to Moses, while Israel moved about in the wilderness. So here I am today, eighty-five years old! I am still as strong today as the day Moses sent me out; I'm just as vigorous to go out to battle now as I was then. Now give me this hill country that the LORD promised me that day. You yourself heard then that the Anakites were there and their cities were large and fortified, but, the LORD helping me, I will drive them out just as he said." Joshua 14:10-12

Caleb could have settled somewhere that was already safe, already comfortable, but he demanded his own promised land, "Give me the hill country!" knowing that God would help him rid it of the giant Anaks. As far as living a healthy and balanced life, what would your "Promised Land" look like?

_____

_____

_____

And what "giants" would you have to fight to rid yourself of their stronghold?

_____

_____

_____

Caleb's story ends that "he followed the Lord wholeheartedly." May we do the same.

"May God himself, the God of peace, sanctify you through and through. May your whole spirit, soul and body be kept blameless at the coming of our Lord Jesus Christ." 1 Thessalonians 5.23 NIV

Father, thank you for caring about every part of us and giving us all we need to stay strong in body and soul for the long haul. In Jesus' Name, Amen.

—— DAY 2: GLORIFY GOD
Lord, I truly want to live in such a way to point others to Your love, grace, and mercy. May all I do glorify You. In Christ's name, Amen.

One of the ways we glorify God, is when the choices we make reflect a firm belief in His will and His way. All those times I choose to trust instead of panic, to say no to that temptation and yes to a better path, to reach out in compassion even when I don't have the right words. In those choices, God takes over *in* me and works *through* me – that which I in my own flesh could never have said or done. And that outpouring shows others that it is God-in-me; thus giving Him all the glory.

WEEK ONE DISCOVER PURPOSE

The apostle Paul was clearly aware of this truth in his own life when he wrote to the people of Corinth. "So whether you eat or drink or whatever you do, do it all for the glory of God." 1 Corinthians 10:31

Perhaps you currently have some eating and drinking habits that do not bring glory to God. As you review your food tracker, what stands out as something that is excessive or needs to be deleted entirely?

_____

_____

_____

Now think about other areas of your life. Paul actually included *"whatever you do, do it all for the glory of God."* Are there any whatevers that you do which, instead of bringing God glory, threaten to tarnish His Name? People are always watching those of us who identify as Christ-followers, wondering if our walk will match our talk. In what areas is it hardest for you to be consistent in God-honoring living?

_____

_____

_____

Read 1 Corinthians 6:19-20 ESV "Or do you not know that your body is a temple of the Holy Spirit within you, whom you have from God? You are not your own, for you were bought with a price. So glorify God in your body."

Paul is reminding us of what three things about our bodies?
1. My body is a _____,
2. The Holy Spirit, third person of the Trinity, which dwells in me was given to me by _____.
3. My body is not _____, because I was _____ by Jesus.

God has purposed that we glorify Him in our bodies. What are some ways you could do that?

_____

_____

_____

The New Testament Greek word used here is *doxon* which is translated to "glory," "honor," "inherent worth." The corresponding Old Testament Hebrew word for glory is *kabo* often translated "weight" or "significance." Thus we often read about the "weight of glory."

Glory is a weight and an inherent worth that belongs only to the Creator and Sustainer of the universe. Not to us be any glory. We know who we are.

Paul describes this well in 2 Corinthians 4:7 "We now have this light shining in our hearts, but we ourselves are like fragile clay jars containing this great treasure. This makes it clear that our great power is from God, not from ourselves."
Based on this Scripture, when an extraordinary light shines forth from a very ordinary vessel, what is the result?

_____
_____
_____

God's people have always been admonished to glorify Him. What three ways are mentioned in Deuteronomy 6:5?

1. _____
2. _____
3. _____

Yesterday we looked at the life of Caleb who went from Egyptian slave to Canaan landowner, surviving forty years of desert wandering. He was remarkable in his strength and his faith, but today I want to remind us that he also lived in such a way that brought glory to God.

Caleb courageously conquered the enemy and made the land of Hebron safe, and when he gave his daughter Aksah in marriage to Othniel, she asked for water to go with her lands and Caleb "gave her the upper and lower springs" as a favor. Numbers 15.19 Generosity of spirit and covenants kept will always bring God glory.

The Hebrew meaning of the name "Caleb" refers to courage, faithful, devotion, wholehearted, bold and brave. What words would you choose to be the meaning of your own name?

_____
_____
_____

"When we live to glorify God, we step into the only true humanizing way of living. We function properly, like a car running on gasoline rather than orange juice. And on top of that, what more enjoyable kind of life is there? How exhausting is the misery of self. How energizing are the joys of living for another?" [1]

"And as God's grace reaches more and more people, there will be great thanksgiving, and God will receive more and more glory." 2 Corinthians 4.15 NLT

Our lives glorify God whenever we allow Him to do things through us that could never have been done in our own efforts. Then all credit and honor go to the One who indwells and empowers us.

_____

_____

_____

Father, You are worthy of all praise and honor and glory. Thank you for filling up my ordinary vessel with Your treasure so I can shine for all the world to see.... You. In Jesus' Name, Amen.

—— DAY 3: INTENTIONAL LIVING
Lord, more and more I realize how fragile life is. Will you help me to make the most of every moment I have, that I might live and love fully? In Christ's name, Amen.

"I really thought I was going to die," Karen whispered, as she recalled her time of hospitalization with COVID-19. Such an experience changes a person. Perhaps you have also been close to the edge, only to return to the land of the living. If so, what was your takeaway?

Karen looked me in the eye and very calmly and firmly stated how important she felt it was to live intentionally. Every single moment. And then she shared Ephesians 5:11-17 with me. Here is the colorful way Eugene Petersen puts it in the Message paraphrase.

"Don't waste your time on useless work, mere busywork, the barren pursuits of darkness. Expose these things for the sham they are. It's a scandal when people waste their lives on things they must do in the darkness where no one will see. Rip the cover off those frauds and see how attractive they look in the light of Christ. Wake up from your sleep, Climb out of your coffins; Christ will show you the light! So watch your step. Use your head. Make the most of every chance you get. These are desperate times! Don't live carelessly, unthinkingly. Make sure you understand what the Master wants."

In these six verses we are given several action steps to take to "understand what the Master wants" – His purpose for us! List each one here, using the above translation:

Don't _____

Expose _____

Rip _____

Wake up _____

Climb out _____

Watch _____

Use _____

Make the _____

Don't _____

Make sure you _____

How do these phrases make you feel about the way you are currently living your life?

_____

_____

_____

THE MESSAGE paraphrase of Proverbs 29:18 is, "If people can't see what God is doing, they stumble all over themselves." Can you relate to that? Some of us have a history of trying the diet of the day, only to toss it aside the moment we trip up. No wonder nothing works. After so many stumbles, many of us just give up—or worse, we give in to whatever feels good. And, frankly, eating sometimes feels good. It's comforting. It numbs us to other things going on in our lives that we aren't ready to address or conquer. But ultimately, it leads to a cycle of shame, guilt and defeat. Psalm 73 speaks to those of us caught in a vicious cycle of destruction. Like the psalmist, we can cry out to God for help. Turn to Psalm 73 and write verses 21-22 below.

_____

_____

God gives four distinct promises in Psalm 73:23-24:

He promises to always be _____.

He promises to hold you _____.

He promises to guide you _____.

He promises to take you _____.

Proverbs 20:18 tells us to do something when we make plans. Why do you think this is important?

As you read Psalm 73:23-26, write out phrases that you can remember to claim on your journey toward health and wholeness.

Have you been just "coasting" through life? Is is time to take seriously some areas which have been pushed aside as you focused on the urgent and expedient?

In C. S. Lewis's *The Screwtape Letters*, the devil meets with his underdevils to plan how best to combat Christianity. Each underdevil is assigned the challenge to come up with a catchy slogan. One suggests "There is no God." The devil feels this would be hard to promote. Another suggests, "There is no devil." Again, the idea is rejected as not possible. The lasts little devil comes up with the slogan, "There is no hurry." [2] What a perfect slogan to defeat Christianity!

Do you find yourself occasionally sidetracked by the "There is no hurry" syndrome? I see this played out daily through the endless obsession with reality television and online social following. Why struggle through your own life when you can vicariously experience someone else's?

That's what I call "armchair living." Don't get involved. Don't try to sing, dance, lose weight, redecorate your home or discipline your own children yourself – let someone else do it and just watch! Then you will have all the enjoyment of the experience with none of the risk, pain, embarrassment or benefits. But not living is slowly dying. Stagnation. Lethargy. Coasting. Settling. Yes, getting out of that armchair is risky. And it's vulnerable to throw yourself into the thick of things with no guarantee about the outcome. Relationships, dreams, faith, health goals – all of these require an element of moving forward with your whole heart!
Whenever I begin a new season of study, I determine to live fully and engage with life. This verse helps me on so many levels. "Because the Sovereign LORD helps me,

I will not be disgraced. Therefore, I have set my face like a stone, determined to do his will. And I know that I will not be put to shame." Isaiah 50:7 NLT

What phrases speak to you from this verse?

_____

_____

_____

Father, thank you for this day of life. May I make wise choices to engage in all You have for me – both to receive and to give back. In Christ's Name, Amen.

—— DAY 4: PURPOSE-DRIVEN

Lord, sometimes I wonder what I have to offer the world today. Will you please open my eyes to all the many ways You created me to serve and share Your love? In Christ's name, Amen.

You might think that a book whose first sentence is "It's not about you.", would rub people the wrong way. Then again, perhaps not. Though we all have our self-centered moments, the truth is most people know (or at least hope) there is more out there than our ordinary little lives. And we want more.

In the twenty years since *The Purpose Driven Life* by Rick Warren was published, it has sold more than 50 million copies worldwide. And this Christian book was on the New York Times Bestseller List for 90 weeks. [3] That's a whole lot of readers hungry to discover their life's purpose. For me, the beauty of this little book lies in its simplicity. Pastor Rick Warren offers forty days of devotions pointing to what he has targeted as five purposes for which God created humans. Today we are going to look at each one, asking God to show us a path for fulfilling that purpose in our own lives.

- **Purpose #1: God Wants Me to Center My Life Around Him – WORSHIP**
  Would you say that God is at the center of your life? Or is He merely relegated to those days when you go to church or Bible Study? Answer this question with a simple drawing showing all the most important facets of your life, noting where God is in the picture.

What does it look like when you worship God wholeheartedly?

_____

_____

_____

_____

*Love the Lord your God with all your heart and with all your soul and with all your mind.'
This is the first and greatest commandment.* Matthew 22:37-38 NIV

- **Purpose #2: God Wants Me to Learn to Love His Family – FELLOWSHIP**
  Are you an active member in a local church? God created us for community
  and we need our sisters and brothers in Christ in order to use our compli-
  mentary gifts to fulfill God's kingdom purposes. Loving the body of Christ
  and serving in fellowship require a level of commitment. How invested are
  you in a local fellowship, and what does that look like?

  _____

  _____

  _____

*And let us consider how we may spur one another on toward love and good deeds, not giv-
ing up meeting together, as some are in the habit of doing, but encouraging one another—
and all the more as you see the Day approaching.* Hebrews 10:24-25 NIV

As you consider the above verse, write down one way you could encourage someone
in your First Place for Health Bible Study group this week.

_____

_____

_____

_____

- **Purpose #3: God Wants Me to Cultivate Spiritual Maturity – DISCIPLESHIP**
  We act on what we know, and when we know more, we act on that. Do you
  know more – both in your head and in your heart – about God and His purposes than you did this time last year? Then, friend, you are growing in faith!
  In Luke 2:40, we learn that Jesus "grew and became strong; he was filled
  with wisdom, and the grace of God was on him."

We exercise regularly and eat healthily so our bodies will grow strong, but just as
Jesus also grew in wisdom and grace, we too should pursue spiritual maturity.

What is one new spiritual practice you have recently incorporated into your life?

_____

_____

Therefore let us move beyond the elementary teachings about Christ and be taken forward to maturity, not laying again the foundation of repentance from acts that lead to death, and of faith in God, Hebrews 6.1 NIV

- **Purpose #4: God Wants Me to Contribute Something Back – MINISTRY**
  Earlier this week we were reminded in Ephesians 2:10 that "We are God's handiwork, created in Christ Jesus to do good works, which God prepared in advance for us to do." God didn't create us just to sit around looking pretty – the gifts, experiences, and opportunities in our lives all converge so that we might use them to serve others through ministry.

Share one way in which you are giving back in your community (church, work, neighborhood, town)?

_____

_____

_____

God has given each of you a gift from his great variety of spiritual gifts. Use them well to serve one another. 1 Peter 4:20 NLT

- **Purpose #5: God Wants Me to Tell Others About His Love - WITNESSING**
  Jesus chose twelve disciples and, through their faithfulness and sacrifice, the number of believers multiplied in such a way that Christianity is still alive today! One person whose life is transformed through an encounter with the living God can turn into throngs of believers. If she speaks up.

Are you sharing your story? Beginning with those in your home and extending to coworkers, neighbors, friends and perhaps even cross culturally. "If someone asks about your hope as a believer, always be ready to explain it." 1 Peter 3:18 NLT
Are you ready to explain your faith? Jot a few notes down here to guide your thoughts:

My life before I came to faith

_____

_____

_____

A situation that turned me to God

_____

_____

_____

My life today as I grow in the Lord

_____

_____

_____

A verse that gives me hope and promise

_____

_____

_____

*All this is from God. Through Christ, God made peace between us and himself, and **God gave us the work of telling everyone about the peace we can have with him. So we have been sent to speak for Christ**. It is as if God is calling to you through us. We speak for Christ when we beg you to be at peace with God.* 2 Corinthians 5:18, 20 NCV

Lord, give me courage and strength for worship, fellowship, discipleship, ministry, and witnessing. Help me to see each of these as part of Your glorious purpose in my life and for Your kingdom. In Christ's Name, Amen.

—— DAY 5: JUSTICE, MERCY, AND HUMILITY

Lord, I long to make a difference in the lives of broken and hurting people. Will You help me understand how to live out justice, mercy, and humility? In Jesus' Name, Amen.

"O people, the LORD has told you what is good, and this is what he requires of you: to do what is right, to love mercy, and to walk humbly with your God." Micah 6:8 NLT
According to this verse, what three things does the Lord require of you?

1. _____

2. _____

3. _____

With regards to your health journey, list a few examples that might flesh out these goals:
I do what is right when I _____

I *love mercy* when I treat myself and others _____
I *walk humbly* with God when my behavior exhibits _____

Today I'd like for us to focus on the middle purpose mentioned in the Micah passage
– love mercy. I have often described grace as "God giving us what we don't deserve"
and mercy as "God not giving us what we do deserve."
What is your current understanding of the word mercy?

_____

_____

_____

I believe that mercy rises as a result of our compassionate understanding of pain. For
those of us who have struggled with temptation, addiction, grief, depression, financial
ruin, or disease, we are the most likely to recognize and empathize with others going
through such things. And through that shared pain, we are prompted by God to offer
mercy.

Read Hebrews 4.14-16 and answer the following questions:
Who is our own high priest? _____

Why does He have a compassionate understanding of our pain?

_____

_____

_____

How, then, do we approach God's throne _____
and what does He give in our time of need?

_____

_____

_____

The Message paraphrase makes it ever so clear – "Take the mercy, accept the help!"
"Now that we know what we have—Jesus, this great High Priest with ready access
to God—let's not let it slip through our fingers. We don't have a priest who is out of
touch with our reality. He's been through weakness and testing, experienced it all—all
but the sin. So let's walk right up to him and get what he is so ready to give. Take the
mercy, accept the help." Hebrews 4.14-16 MSG

Jesus knows the reality of our lives. God became human in order to save other humans. This required that He become familiar in every way of what it is like to be human. Every way, except choosing to sin. No matter what you have gone through thus far, be assured that Jesus knows and understands. It does not surprise Him that we are weak, that we have failed. He is the Lord of second chances.

Where do you stand in need of mercy today?

_____

_____

_____

At First Place for Health, we love stories. Especially stories of how we were, how we are now, and all that happened in between. Look no further than our monthly newsletter and even those in your group for before and after testimonies to God's faithfulness and fruit.

The prophet Hosea shows us one side of God's heart of mercy to a people who continually seek to thwart His purpose in their lives. In Hosea 11:7 what is God lamenting about His people?

_____

_____

_____

When you think of the times you also chose to go your own way instead of following what you knew to be God's wisdom, how do you feel?

_____

_____

_____

Listen to God's heart of compassion and mercy: *My heart recoils within me; my compassion grows warm and tender. I will not execute my burning anger; I will not again destroy Ephraim; for I am God and not a man, the Holy One in your midst, and I will not come in wrath.* Hosea 11:8-9 ESV

God has chosen to extend mercy to us ("I will not come in wrath") and asks that, in turn, we become people who do "what is right," "love mercy," and "walk humbly" with Him. What choices could you make this week toward that end?

Lord, I am eternally grateful for Your heart of compassion and mercy toward me and all Your creation. May I learn how to humbly walk with You each step of my journey. In Christ's Name, Amen.

—— DAY 6: REFLECTION AND APPLICATION

Lord, I want to choose what's best, but often I fall back into unhealthy patterns. Please direct my paths today toward balance and blessing. In Christ's name, Amen.

When people do not accept divine guidance, they run wild. But whoever obeys the law is joyful. Proverbs 29:18 NLT

Can you think of a time when you ran wild – choosing your own way instead of the path you knew God had for you? Write down what happened and the consequences.

God's law is for our good. So even if we hate being told what to do (and not do) the Bible says that obedience brings joy. Keeping the law is a conscious choice. For many centuries, Christ-followers have learned how to follow God's law by observing spiritual disciplines such as Bible study, devotional reading, prayer, Scripture meditation and memorization, worship and fellowship, journaling, communion and more. These habits help us become more like Jesus. This is called "sanctification."

Sanctification is a building process; it doesn't happen all at once. You chose to open this Bible study book today because you decided in your mind first (and the rest of you followed) to study God's Word and pursue balance in the four areas of health. You could have chosen otherwise. Congratulations!

Psalm 119 is the longest chapter in the Bible, and it's all about the benefits of choosing to keep God's law. Turn to verses 1-2 and write down who is blessed.

In what ways have you been blessed this week by practicing some of the spiritual disciplines mentioned above? Try to pinpoint at least one blessing in each of the four areas.

Physical	Mental
Spiritual	**Emotional**

Are there certain "triggers"—times of the day or places or even people— that make it difficult for you to choose obedience? If so, what are those triggers?

_____

_____

_____

The psalmist makes a choice in Psalm 119:30-32. What does he choose to do?

_____

_____

_____

Do any of the verbs in those verses, such as "chosen," "set my heart," "hold fast" and "run" describe your life in these early weeks of seeking a more balanced life? How?

_____

_____

_____

If you read further in Psalm 119 to verses 33-39, the psalmist asks God to do eight things so that he might be blessed. List these below:

Teach me _____

Give me _____

Direct me _____

Turn my heart _____

Turn my eyes _____

Preserve my _____

Fulfill Your _____

Take away _____

A few years ago, I decided to try an experiment: I would seek to satisfy my spiritual hunger before my physical hunger. So, every morning, I woke up early to do my Bible study and prayer before breakfast. By noting in my journal one benefit from those sessions, I've been able to make food and eating a secondary focus in starting my day. God's promises come first. Fast forward to today and it's already a habit.

Almighty God, You satisfy me with good things. Thank You for all I'm learning from the Bible—may it satisfy my deep hunger. In Christ's name, Amen.

—— DAY 7: REFLECTION AND APPLICATION

Lord, I desperately want my efforts to achieve long-lasting success. Please do whatever is necessary to help me persevere with power. Amen.

When Hezekiah was told he would soon die, he cried, *Remember, LORD, how I have walked before you faithfully and with wholehearted devotion and have done what is good in your eyes.* Isaiah 38:3 NIV

God heard this wholehearted plea and gave him more years of life. Are you wholehearted in your desire to do the work of discovering God's purpose for your life on all levels? The reason this is so important is that sometimes we choose to "dabble" instead of buying into the whole program. Yet, I've discovered the hard way that complete commitment is the only path to success.

Have you also known people who pick and choose when it comes to wholeness? They decide on their own modifications which meet their own needs. One woman in my group did such a thing and shared with me a testimony to growth: "Oops! After realizing that my 'modifications' were really just excuses, I committed to do everything the First Place for Health team recommended, just like a little child. As soon as I pried my fingers of control off the situation, it became a delight. And yes, I've memorized all four verses so far. It's coming to this as a child that's working for me." We seek wellness for many reasons – incentivized by an upcoming wedding or reunion; frightened by a medical diagnosis; or even shame from well-meaning comments that crush our spirits and cause us to decide, *I'll show them!*

God has used a variety of ways to get my attention, but those kinds of reasons don't usually cause victory for me. I begin halfheartedly and go down from there. To achieve anything truly important and long lasting, I must do it with my whole heart.

Write down Psalm 119:10-11 below.

_____

_____

_____

In these verses, what two things does the psalmist say about his heart in his endeavor to follow God?

_____

_____

_____

Is there any part of your heart that is holding back from being fully committed to living differently based on God's will and God's way? If so, why?

_____

_____

_____

Do you need God's help in committing wholeheartedly to Him? Write down Psalm 119:145-146 as a prayer to Him:

_____

_____

_____

Gracious God, I am determined to be faithful for the long haul. Help me to embrace You fully while I put Christ first in my life and follow this new regimen. In Christ's name, Amen.

Notes

1. Dane Ortlund, "Gentle and Lowly" (Wheaton IL: Crossway, 2020) 205.

2. C.S. Lewis, "The Screwtape Letters" (HarperSanFrancisco, 2001)

3. https://saddleback.com/connect/Articles/MAP/2019/1/23/GODS-5-PURPOSES-FOR-YOUR-LIFE

WEEK TWO: DESIRE CHANGE

SCRIPTURE MEMORY VERSE
May he give you the desire of your heart and make all your plans succeed. Psalm 20:4

What do you want? If you could reach deep into your soul and identify your greatest longing, what would it be? Now, be honest and give a true answer. Ask God to help you peel away the layers of your heart and show you what appears to be your most important desire, even if you don't totally understand the state of your heart right now.

My deepest desire is _____.

We live each day in response to our deepest desires. The good news is that, at least for the past week, First Place for Health has been part of your life plan—and it's likely this choice reflects your deep desire to live a healthy life. You have invested time, energy, and resources to draw closer to God and seek His way for your physical, mental, spiritual, and emotional health. But now you may be at the point where the newness and excitement has faded and you need a fresh commitment to the journey of change.

Do you really want change? As you look at your life (relationships, time with God, eating, exercise) do you see any areas that need revamping and retooling? The next question is how much you want to change. Because unless you truly, deeply desire change with your whole heart, you will never be able to keep going through the confusing midst of it in order to emerge on the other side.

Change is hard. Even wanted change can bring on almost insurmountable adjustments. But feelings of frustration and failure can and should lead us to the arms of Christ, who welcomes and comforts us with the knowledge that we don't have to live this new life alone. He is beside us each step of the way, guiding and empowering with divine provision!

Will you come before Him with a still and quiet spirit today, believing that God knows your desires and plans for necessary changes in the various areas of your life?

—— DAY 1: YOUR DEEPEST DESIRE

Lord, sometimes I don't even know what I should desire. Please help me to understand and pinpoint godly desires and dreams for my life. In Christ's name, Amen.

Some say that if you want to know what is truly important in a person's life, ask how they spend their time and money. Our checkbooks, planners, and even cell phones can be quite revealing.

What do your checkbook, planner, and screen time reveal about what's most important to you?

_____

_____

_____

In the introduction to this week's study, what did you write as your deepest desire? This is important to determine, because if you don't know what it is, how will you know when God grants it?

_____

_____

_____

Psalm 37:4-6 reminds us that even though there is often bad news all around, God will bring justice for His people in His own way and His own time. There is a caveat, however—something each of us must do in order for that to happen. Read those verses and fill in the blanks, which are the actions we must take:

_____ _____ _____ _____ _____ *and he will*

give you the desires of your heart.

_____ _____ _____ _____ _____ _____; _____ ____

_____ _____ _____ _____ *and he will do this: He will make your righteousness*

shine like the dawn, the justice of your cause like the noonday sun.

What do you think is meant by "delight yourself in the Lord"?

_____

_____

_____

What is one way you could do that today?

_____

_____

_____

Which is the hardest for you --- to "commit your way to the Lord" or to "trust Him"? Why?

_____

_____

_____

Heavenly Father, I do commit myself to You in a fresh way today. Please help me learn to trust You with every detail of my life. In Christ's name, Amen.

—— DAY 2: DO YOU WANT TO GET WELL?
Lord, I'm dizzy from living a roller-coaster lifestyle. You know my heart, so please help me be willing to be willing. In Christ's name, Amen.

I find great comfort in the assurance that God knows my heart even when I'm not sure what's happening deep down inside. Even now, He knows your hopes and dreams as you study *God's Purpose for You*. But while He recognizes that you are taking steps towards a more balanced life, you may still need to take stock of your full intentions and answer this question: "Do you want to get well?"

Read John 5:1-9. Years ago I was privileged to visit Jerusalem and the deep pool called Bethesda. Over the centuries, land has built up and there no longer remains a refreshing and healing spa as was present in Jesus' day.

Who was gathered around the pool at Bethesda?

_____

_____

_____

One invalid had been there for a long time. How long had he waited for healing? Why had it been so long (v. 7)?

_____

_____

_____

At the time, people believed that this pool had healing powers whenever the waters were stirred up. However, unless someone carried this man and placed him in the stirred-up waters, he had no hope for healing. What do you think this man's state of mind was when Jesus approached him as he was lying helplessly by the pool?

_____

_____

_____

Do you think Jesus knew why the man was there? Do you think Jesus knew what was in the man's heart? What did Jesus say to him (v. 6)?

_____

_____

_____

Sometimes we can get so used to being the way we are that it becomes part of our identity. We cling to what we know rather than taking the risk to pursue real change in our lives. In what ways might you be enslaved to the status quo and fearful of pursuing true change?

_____

_____

_____

If Jesus were to ask you today, "Do you want to get well?" what would be your answer? Write down the words you would say to Him if you could.

_____

_____

_____

How did the man respond (v. 7)? Did he answer Jesus' question?

_____

_____

_____

Jesus didn't argue with the man, but He did ask him to do something. What did he ask him to do (v. 8)?

_____

_____

_____

The first two words in verse 9 are: _____

Wow! What was the first thing the man did?

_____
_____
_____

Later, even though Jesus' healing on the Sabbath had been controversial, what did the man go on to do (vv. 11 and 15)?

_____
_____
_____

Dearest Jesus, I've been lying by the pool for so long and now I'm ready to answer You. Do whatever it takes—I want to get well! Amen.

—— DAY 3: YOUR PLANS, GOD'S PLANS

Lord, too often I react rather than respond. My life in some areas is so haphazard that I'm spinning in circles. Please help me focus. Amen.

Are you a control freak? Do you love to write down plans and fill in your schedule for weeks, months and sometimes years in advance, secretly believing that if you write it down, somehow you can control it? Any of us who struggle with control issues should memorize the wisdom found in Proverbs 19:21. Write that verse below:

_____
_____
_____

God doesn't want me to offer Him my plans so that He can rubber stamp them with His approval and send me on my way. He does, however, want me to plan. And then He wants me to offer up those plans to Him as an act of relinquishment, believing in faith that He will either bless them or redirect me.

What does this week's memory verse say about our plans? Why do you think we have a tendency to make so many of them?

_____
_____
_____

Why do you think First Place for Health includes the discipline of keeping a Live It Tracker?

_____

_____

_____

What have you observed about your eating plans as you've used your Live It Tracker?

_____

_____

_____

My wise grandmother once remarked, "If you don't know where you're going, you'll get there every time!" How can using the Live It Tracker help you get where you want to go?

_____

_____

_____

Read Proverbs 16:9. Record what your role is and what God's role is:

In his heart _____ , but the Lord _____

_____ .

Can you think of a time when you made plans in your heart, plans you thought would be pleasing to God, only to have Him direct your steps in a totally different direction? What happened?

_____

_____

_____

At some point in life, many of us encounter a season of unemployment. Perhaps you are one of those who are now in-between jobs. If so, perhaps you've heard the old saying: "God can't steer a parked car!" It's up to us to get the job hunt process moving—filling out applications, interviewing, praying, networking and asking God to open doors or close doors as He directs. We have our part to do; just sitting around the house waiting for the right job to drop down from the sky isn't realistic.

We can also apply this principle to our pursuit of balanced living. What do you see as your part for moving forward on your health journey?

_____
_____
_____

What do you see as God's part?

_____
_____
_____

As we grow closer to God through prayer, Bible Study, worship, and obedience, the easier it will be to determine the purposes of His heart. Read Psalm 33:11. What does God promise in this verse?

_____
_____
_____

As you begin to release your plans to God, you become a model of obedience to the next generation. If your child (or any young person) asked you today, "Does God really have a plan?" how would you respond?

_____
_____
_____

Lord, I am ready to give up control of my life. Fill me with the good things You have planned for me. Thank You for helping me move forward. Amen.

—— DAY 4: INNER TRANSFORMATION

Lord, when I look in the mirror, I hardly recognize that person. Help me to get my outer body and inner soul aligned together in such a way that You may be glorified. In Christ's name, Amen.

At my very first (but certainly not my last) First Place for Health Wellness Week in Texas back in 2007, I walked with then director Carole Lewis and another woman each morning. Carole was a big encouragement to both of us to walk slowly and stretch our limits as the week went on. My new friend from Kansas went back home and kept going and going and going, and when she showed up at Wellness Week the next year . . . there were 100 pounds less of her to walk each morning!

What a huge accomplishment for only one year! But her outward transformation was really just a manifestation of the changes God had made in her inwardly. What a great perk! If we follow a lifestyle that puts Christ first, change will happen on the inside and outside.

_____

_____

_____

Read Romans 12:1-2. Paul encourages us to offer ourselves to God in this passage. What words does he use to describe the offering of our bodies (v. 1)?

Living _____ , holy and _____

_____ _____

Have you ever thought of your body in such a way? How does this description make you feel?

_____

_____

_____

In verse 2, Paul gives further instructions. What does he tell us we should and should not do? What will be the result of this choice?

_____

_____

_____

The word "transformed" in verse 2 comes from the Greek word *metamorphoo*, from which we also get our English word "metamorphosis." The transformation God desires is a process of morphing into Christ-likeness, a total change from one thing to a distinct other. Where does this morphing start in us (v. 2)?

_____

_____

_____

We must first decide in our minds that we are ready, willing, and able to meet the challenge. What if you magically lost all your excess pounds and were immediately outwardly transformed? Would your unchanged inner life have an effect on your ability to keep it off? How does your mind and heart need to change in order to be successful for the long haul?

_____
_____
_____

Does Paul ask you to do anything in this passage that is too hard? Why?

_____
_____
_____

Think about the areas in your mind and heart that need inner transformation. Offer these to God and ask Him to do the *metamorphoo* work in you—to change you from the inside out!

Heavenly Father, please help me get rid of those things in my mind and heart that hinder my spiritual growth. I lay my whole life before You and ask You to change me from the inside out. In Christ's name, Amen

—— DAY 5: EMPOWERED FOR SUCCESS

Lord, without divine intervention, I'll never be successful in my efforts. Please grant me Your Holy Spirit power to persevere and prevail. Amen.

At some point on our journey toward a balanced life, many of us find ourselves thinking, *This is just too hard. I can't do it. I just can't. I do well for a little while, then I give in to old patterns and feel like giving up all together. It's just too hard.*

Hey, we've all been there, and many of us have given in to discouragement and despair at failing yet another attempt for lasting health. This usually happens because we're trusting in our strength alone. Let's face it: some of us are pretty strong and can keep going for quite a while. But the truth is, lasting change is too difficult to accomplish in our own strength. That is why God sent the Holy Spirit—to empower every believer to accomplish far more than we ever could by ourselves. Read Romans 15:13. What are two results of trusting in God?

_____
_____
_____

While this is a silly analogy, it helps me understand divine power. Think about vacuuming. If you push and pull the vacuum back and forth across your carpet, it may leave trails through the fibers that make your floor appear clean. But if you don't *plug your vacuum in*, no dirt is removed! The same is true for your journey toward a whole and healthy life—you need *power*!

Read 2 Corinthians 3:18. Here, Paul talks about us being transformed into Christ's likeness with an ever-increasing glory. From what source does transformation come to us, according to Paul?

_____

_____

_____

Are you depending on God to change you through the power of the Holy Spirit, or have you been striving to do it on your own? What are three specific steps you can take to "plug in" to divine power today?

_____

_____

_____

One of the most amazing truths about the life of faith is that God uses ordinary people to do extraordinary things. Take the apostle Paul, for example. Even though he had incredible intellectual credentials, they were not what he depended on to spread the Good News of Christ. Read 1 Corinthians 2:3-5. What was the reason Paul relied on the Spirit's power (v. 5)?

_____

_____

_____

Remember: you can be successful in your quest to know God's purpose, but it is up to you to decide to appropriate God's power and provision.

Lord, in every crisis of my life, You have been there for me. Thank You that, through Your power, I can now serve and succeed. In Christ's name, Amen.

—— DAY 6: REFLECTION AND APPLICATION
Lord, I seek a fuller life than the one I'm currently living. Help me to cast aside anything that holds me back from Your best. In Christ's name, Amen.

In *The Journey of Desire*, John Eldredge states that the reason most of us don't actually know what we want is that we're so unacquainted with our desire.1

Is this true in your life? What is buried in your soul—buried because you dare not release it, just in case it's beyond reach and you're not sure you want to live with that kind of disappointment? Have you given up hope that your deepest desire might actually be from God, and therefore a gift? Are you willing to begin digging deep, chipping away at the protective walls that guard your heart from further disappointment and pain? What do you think you would uncover?

_____

_____

_____

All too often we have sought life in all kinds of things other than God. Some of us, if we are brave enough to admit it, have even sought solace through eating—filling a void. When that happens, everything in us may be saying, *But I really want to eat that whole carton of ice cream—that seems like life to me right now.* God says, *I know you do, but it will kill you in the end. What you think is life is not. That's not the comfort [or love or significance] you are seeking. You'll wind up destroying yourself.* So, next time you find yourself seeking something other than God for spiritual satisfaction, remember to line up your desires with what God reveals to you in His Word.

What has God's Word—God's law—shown you is best for your life so far?

_____

_____

_____

One definition of "desire" is a *longing for something.* "Longing" is a pretty strong word isn't it? It's more descriptive than just "wanting"—it connotes desperation for something. Do you long to be changed from the inside out? Share your feelings about this in a letter to God, your heavenly Father, either below or in your journal.

Jesus, help turn me from that which diminishes life to that which brings life. Give me hope that I can truly be changed. In Christ's name, Amen.

—— DAY 7: REFLECTION AND APPLICATION
Lord, I want to believe that You have a plan and a purpose for my life. Help me to hold on to this promise. In Christ's name, Amen.

MYplace O FOR BIBLE STUDY

This week we learned that in order to embrace God's way, we must let go of seeking control. One practical exercise that may help you do this is to kneel by your bedside in prayer and open your hands. Envision yourself kneeling at the feet of Jesus as you release everyone and every situation to your Lord and Master, opening your hands to show that you're giving up control. (Of course, being in control is really an illusion—we never are in control; we just think we are.)

With empty hands, you are ready to receive from Him exactly what He wants to give—His will, His way, in His time. It may help to repeat the words from the Lord's Prayer: *Your will be done. Your will be done.*

This week's memory verse concludes with the phrase "and make all your plans succeed." What would that look like for you?

A promise from God is found in Jeremiah 29:11. What are the four purposes for you of God's plans, as outlined in this verse?

Spend some time today—at least 20 minutes—writing in your journal. Be specific about your goals (short term and long term) and your vision of your life when your desires have been fulfilled. As we progress together through *God's Purpose for You*, use your journal to write letters and prayers to God, and to record verses that become especially meaningful to you.

Gracious God, direct my thoughts and my pen as I seek to plan for success. I will give my all and trust You with the results. In Christ's name, Amen.

Notes

1. John Eldredge, The Journey of Desire: Searching for the Life We've Only Dreamed Of (Nashville, TN: Thomas Nelson Publishers, 2000).

WEEK THREE: LOVE GOD

SCRIPTURE MEMORY VERSE
*Love the **LORD** your God with all your heart and with all your soul and with all your strength. Deuteronomy 6:5*

Are you a God-lover? Your first reaction to this question may be, "Of course I love God!" But, as this week's verse reminds us, our love for God should consume our whole being—heart, soul and strength. Do you love God like that?

In Deuteronomy 6:5, God commanded the Israelites to love Him with every part of them. What would loving God look like for you in these three areas?

All your heart:

_____
_____
_____

All your soul:

_____
_____
_____

All your strength:

_____
_____
_____

Look up Mark 12:30. This verse is Jesus' answer to what question posed by what group of people (vv. 28-29)? What was his answer?

_____
_____
_____
_____

Do you think what Jesus deemed as "the greatest commandment" might be important for you to obey too? If so, how do you think you are currently doing on "loving God totally"?

_____

_____

—— DAY 1: WHAT GOD REQUIRES

Heavenly Father, help me today to love You with my heart, soul and strength. In Christ's name, Amen.

Read Deuteronomy 10:11-13. Write out verses 12-13 below, underlining each word that indicates a command by God (there are five).

_____

_____

_____

In Deuteronomy 10, Moses is reminding the people of Israel how God gave him the Ten Commandments at Mount Sinai. Moses' job was to come back down from the mountain and do what (v. 11)?

_____

_____

_____

Then, in verses 12-13, Moses reminds the Israelites what they are required to do in order to inherit and inhabit the Promised Land. As you think of your health journey, what would you say is your "promised land"—the "place" you are seeking?

_____

_____

_____

How can you fulfill these commands and arrive in your promised land?

Fear the Lord:

_____

_____

_____

Love Him:

_____

_____

_____

Walk in His ways:

_____

_____

_____

Serve the Lord with all your heart and soul:

_____

_____

_____

Observe the Lord's commands and decrees:

_____

_____

_____

When words and phrases are often repeated in the Bible, they indicate great importance. Throughout the Old Testament, God is adamant about His requirements for His people. Look up the following verses and write below the commands in them.

Deuteronomy 11:1:

_____

_____

_____

Deuteronomy 30:20:

_____

_____

_____

Joshua 22:5:

_____

_____

_____

Joshua 23:11:

_____
_____
_____.

Gracious God, thank You for going before me into the "promised land" of Your pur-
pose in my life. May I follow with joy and obedience. Amen.

—— DAY 2: OBEDIENCE

Dearest Jesus, I want to obey You as an act of love. Help that love to flow from every
part of me today. In Christ's name, Amen.

Read John 14:21. How does God know that we love Him?

_____
_____
_____

What does the disciple Jesus loved, John, say will happen to those who obey God's
commands (see the second half of verse 21)?

_____
_____
_____

Having read some of God's commands yesterday, how would you evaluate your love
of God, based on John's words?

_____
_____
_____

Why do you think it's so hard to love Him with every part instead of just those parts
we are willing to surrender at any given time?

_____
_____
_____

Author Nancie Carmichael points out that "Jesus said we are to love Him with our
body, mind, soul and spirit. That means loving Him with our whole selves, not just
some splintered-off part."[1]

One way to look at our response is to consider that we are like houses with four rooms—body, soul, mind and spirit—and to realize that to be a truly balanced person, we must tidy up each of these rooms every day. Write down what you can do today in each of your four rooms to straighten them up.

Body	Mind
Spirit	Soul

Thank You, Father, for helping me find balance in all areas of my life. In Christ's name, Amen.

—— DAY 3: BELIEF SYSTEM

Almighty God, I know that Your commands are there for my good. May I follow them completely and joyfully. In Christ's name, Amen.

Read 1 John 5:1-3. In verse 1, John tells us another requirement for loving God: "believing that Jesus is the Christ." Describe when and where you first believed this.

John also adds a further proof of our love for God: those of us who love God will love others and by loving others, we will know we love God. How do you think loving others is an extension of loving God?

If you asked God to help you love others to demonstrate your love for Him, how do you think He might enable you to do this?

_____
_____
_____

What does John remind us in verse 3?

_____
_____
_____

Do you ever find God's commands to be a burden? If so, which ones?

_____
_____
_____

What about the First Place for Health guidelines? Do any seem burdensome to you and, if so, why?

_____
_____
_____

It may be that your current belief system needs some overhauling so that you can come to believe what is true through God's Word. Carole Lewis, First Place for Health national director emeritus, shares that the secret for balanced health begins with the belief that *God is good*:

> God is good is one of the most far-reaching principles of the Bible, and it affects your life in ways that you may never have imagined.
>
> Nahum 1:7 says "The Lord is good, a refuge in times of trouble, He cares for those who trust in Him." That's the real answer to your goal of losing weight and becoming healthy. Start with the fact that God is good. He cares for you. The answer you're looking for encompasses not just taking off the pounds, but also living the life of purpose and hope you were meant to live. This is the life God calls you to live. And that life is well within your grasp.[2]

Do you truly believe, deep down, that God is good? If there is a part of you that is hesitant, why do you think you are reluctant to believe?

_____

_____

_____

Gracious God, truly You are good and want good things for me. Help me to believe that today and always. In Christ's name, Amen.

—— DAY 4: ACTIONS

Holy Spirit, reveal to me specific actions I can take today in order to show my love as a follower of Jesus. In Christ's name, Amen.

Read 1 John 3:18-20. Verse 18 admonishes us to not love merely with

_____ or _____ but with

_____ and in _____.

The latest edition of *Merriam Webster's Collegiate Dictionary* includes a new word that comes to mind when I read this verse—frenemy. The definition of "frenemy" is "someone who acts like a friend but is really an enemy."[3]

_____

_____

_____

In other words, they may say all the right "friendly" words, but their "enemy" actions reveal otherwise. In your journey toward balanced health, can you think of a time when you "talked the talk" but didn't "walk the walk"?

_____

_____

_____

Mother Teresa, who ministered to the dying in Calcutta and organized the Missionaries of Charity in more than 52 countries, provided this insight into what it means to live by actions:

> I never look at the masses as my responsibility. I look at the individual. I can love only one person at a time. I can feed only one person at a time. Just one, one,

one. As Jesus said, "Whatever you do to the least of my brethren, you do it to me." So I begin. I picked up one person. The whole work is only a drop in the ocean. But if we don't put the drop in, the ocean would be one drop less. Same thing for you. Same thing in your family. Same thing in the church where you go. Just begin -- one, one, one![4]

Read 1 John 3:19-20. How do these verses encourage you that loving God in both word and deed is possible, even if you have failed before?

_____
_____
_____

Is your heart "at rest" in the presence of God? Take some time to sit in silence and just pour out your love to Him, not asking anything in return.

Heavenly Father, may I know that with every choice I make, I can make a difference in someone's life today. Let it be a good difference. Amen.

—— DAY 5: SOURCE OF LOVE
Lord, even though I've never actually seen You, I trust You for every need today and I want You to know that I love You. In Christ's name, Amen.

Read 1 John 4:7-16. What is the source of love, and to whom is it available (vv. 7-8)?

_____
_____
_____

In the first four days of this week, we have looked at the following areas. How are they spelled out again in this day's passage of Scripture?

Day 1—What God Requires (1 John 4:15-16)

_____
_____

Day 2—Obedience (1 John 4:9)

_____
_____

Day 3—Belief System (1 John 4:10,14)

_____

_____

_____

Day 4—Actions (1 John 4:11-12)

_____

_____

_____

If we don't love, what does this say about us and why (v. 8)?

_____

_____

_____

What did God do to show how much He loves us (vv. 9-10)?

_____

_____

_____

What should be our response to God's action of love (v. 11)?

_____

_____

_____

Name two things that happen when we invite God's love into our hearts:

verse 12:

_____

_____

verse 15:

_____

_____

If you've experienced God's love in your life, when was the last time you shared that good news (v. 14)? How will you testify to His love today?

_____

_____

_____

Gracious God, please clearly open a way for me to share Your love with someone today who desperately needs to know that good news. Amen.

—— DAY 6: REFLECTION AND APPLICATION

Lord, I am a fearful person much of the time and I don't understand why. Will You deliver me from fear into faith? In Christ's name, Amen.

Read 1 John 4:17-21. What happens when God's love is made complete in us (v. 17)?

_____

_____

_____

Why do you think some people are afraid that God doesn't love them?

_____

_____

_____

What are your greatest fears today?

_____

_____

_____

_____

Why does fear have no place in the heart of anyone who loves God totally (v. 18)?

_____

_____

_____

How might being a fearful person affect your ability to be a loving person?

_____

_____

_____

Do you believe God is greater than your greatest fears? If you are afraid of anything in your First Place for Health journey, name those fears and pray right now that God will deliver you from them. Write your prayer in the following space or in your journal.

_____
_____
_____
_____
_____

In our goal to love God totally, we must also seek to be loving toward those around us. How is our love of God related to our love of others (see v. 20)?

_____
_____
_____

One way of loving God is to love our sisters and brothers (see v. 21). Think of someone you have a hard time loving. Now, commit to pray for that person for each day this week and see if your heart toward them changes.

God, You know that sometimes loving others is hard for me. Help me today to love with the same love You have so graciously extended to me. Amen.

—— DAY 7: REFLECTION AND APPLICATION

Heavenly Father, sometimes I have a hard time understanding how You could love me unconditionally. Thank You for showing me every day that You really do! In Christ's name, Amen.

First John 4:19 says, "We love because He first loved us." Do you know how much God loves you? As you familiarize yourself with the character of God, you will discover that His nature is Love—His love for us is a "sure thing"!

_____
_____
_____

Perhaps a study on the attributes of God will help you understand that God's love for you enables you to respond in kind with love for Him. God is with us along our journey toward balanced living and health. Like the old saying goes, "God loves us as we are, but loves us too much to let us stay there."

Three words describe the greatness of who God is and what He can do. Look these up in a dictionary and write their definitions below each characteristic of God.

Omniscient:

_____
_____
_____

Omnipotent:

_____
_____
_____

Omnipresent:

_____
_____
_____

Which one of these traits of God do you need to rely on or embrace in a special way this week?

_____
_____
_____

As you continue to seek to love God totally, may these scriptural promises to you in the form of a love letter from God give you courage and strength to further embrace His purposes for your life:

Dear [your name],

Before the beginning of time, I knew you. I knew what color your eyes would be, and I could hear the sound of your laughter. Like a proud father who carries a picture of His daughter, I carried the image of you in My eyes, for you were created in My image. Before the beginning of time, I chose you. I spoke your name into the heavens and I smiled as its melody resounded off the walls of My heart. You are Mine. My love for you extends farther than the stars in the sky and deeper than any ocean. You are My pearl of great price, the one for whom I gave everything. I cradle you in the palm of My hand. I love you even in the face of your failure. Nothing you can say or do can cause Me to stop loving you. I am ruthless in My pursuit of you. Run from Me— I will love you. Spurn Me—I will love you. Reject yourself—I will love you. You see, My love for you was slain before the foundations of the world and I have never regretted the sacrifice I made for you at Calvary.

When I see every part of who You are, I marvel at the work of My hands, for I whispered words of longing and desire and you came into existence. You are beautiful, and I take pleasure in you—heart, mind, and body. You are my desire. When you turn your head in shame and despise what I have made, still I reach for you with gentle passion. You are My beloved and I am yours.

Love, Your heavenly Father.[5]

Jesus, truly You are the Lover of my soul. I love you back, now and forever. In Christ's name, Amen.

Notes

1. Nancy Carmichael, Praying for Rain (Nashville, TN: Thomas Nelson Publishers, 2001), p. 62.

2. Carole Lewis, First Place 4 Health (Ventura, CA: Gospel Light Publishers, 2008), pp. 25-26.

3. "frenemy," Merriam-Webster Online Dictionary, http://www.merriam-webster.com/ dictionary/ frenemy.

4. Mother Teresa, quoted in Susan Conroy, Mother Teresa's Lessons of Love and Secrets of Sanctity (Huntington, IN: Our Sunday Visitor Publishing Division, 2003), p. 205.

5. Regina Franklin, Who Calls Me Beautiful? (Grand Rapids, MI: Discovery House Publishers, 2004), pp. 44-45. (Based on Psalm 194:4; Song of Solomon 7:10,63; Isaiah 43:1; Matthew 13:46; Ephesians 1:4; 1 John 3:2; Revelation 13:8.)

WEEK FOUR: STAND STRONG

SCRIPTURE MEMORY VERSE
Put on the full armor of God so that you can take your stand against the devil's schemes. Ephesians 6:11

For me, it often begins as a niggling doubt, a false truth I start to believe, and gradually escalates into taunts reminiscent of a hiss. Yes, there is an enemy of my soul, and knowing all my weak points, he schemes to trip me up where I'm most vulnerable. It wasn't until I was an adult that I confronted the true reality of spiritual warfare. The more I sought to live with Christ as both Lord and Savior, the greater the battle.

It helped greatly as I began to dig deep and identify areas of my life where I'd always felt defeated; places I had to return to over and over again. These strongholds seemed impenetrable on my own. As you begin memorizing this week's verse and studying about God's purpose for us to stand strong, ask God to show you if the enemy of your soul (the devil) has established any strongholds in your life.

Beth Moore describes a stronghold as "anything that exalts itself in our minds 'pretending' to be bigger or more powerful than our God. It steals much of our focus and causes us to feel overpowered. Controlled. Mastered. Whether the stronghold is an addiction, unforgiveness toward a person who has hurt us, or despair over loss, it is something that consumes so much of our emotional and mental energy that abundant life is strangled—or callings remain largely unfulfilled and our believing lives are virtually ineffective."[1]

Strongholds are false, negative messages that hold us down and prevent us from conquering destructive patterns and lifestyles. Here are a few possible areas of strongholds. Prayerfully ask God to reveal to you if any of these (or others you could add in the blanks) are currently battling for your soul. Put a check mark by any of the following strongholds at work in your life:

- O Depression
- O Anger
- O Insecurity
- O Unforgiveness

○   Addictions
○   Witchcraft
○   Sexual impurity
○   Fear
○   Bitterness
○   Jealousy
○   Pride
○   Shame
○   Other_____

—— DAY 1: PREPARED FOR BATTLE

Mighty God, please fight for me as I seek to demolish strongholds that have been in my life for a very long time. In Christ's name, Amen.

Are you finding it hard to keep the First Place for Health commitments to healthy eating, exercising, memorizing God's Word, praying for others and Bible study?

Who do you think wants you to fail in each of these areas?

_____
_____
_____

Who do you think wants you to be victorious in each of these areas?

_____
_____
_____

Read Ephesians 6:10-18. Who is our struggle against (v. 12)?

_____
_____
_____

God promises to fight life's battles for us and with us. He also gives us important tools for standing against all opposition. The apostle Paul loved God's people in the town of Ephesus, but he knew that they were sorely tempted to give in to the ways of the world and go against God's teachings. So, Paul wrote to them using the imagery of battle and armor, hoping they would understand the concept of "putting on" spiritual armor each day as they sought to live for Christ. With that in mind, complete this table.

God's Tool	Piece of Armor	What It Does For Us
Truth	Belt	
Righteousness	Breastplate	
Gospel of Peace	Feel of Readiness	
Faith	Shield	
Salvation	Helmet	
Word of God	Sword of the Spirit	

Verse 18 gives three final admonitions to remember as we go into battle. What are they?

1. _____
2. _____
3. _____

Several years ago, author John Eldredge was honored at a book convention with a large sword, as big as the one his *Braveheart* hero, William Wallace, used in Scotland many years ago. John loved it because it represented his core belief that all Christ-followers must be prepared to do battle for their very lives. "We are at war," he said:

> This is a Love Story set in the midst of a life and death battle. Look around you at all the casualties strewn across the fields, the lost souls, the broken hearts, the captives. We must take this battle seriously—it is a war for the human heart. You have a crucial role to play. Many have underestimated their roles in the Story but that is dangerous. You will lose heart and you will miss your cues.[2]

Thank You, God, for all the armor You provide—I promise to put it on every single day! In Christ's name, Amen.

—— DAY 2: THE ENEMY
Dear Lord, speaking of Satan is sometimes frightening to me. Help me remember that You are more powerful. In Christ's name, Amen.

Read 1 Peter 5:8-11. In verse 8, Peter warns us to cultivate two important character- istics. What are they? Why are they important?

_____

_____

_____

According to verse 9, what are we to do? Why?

_____

_____

_____

Does verse 10 indicate that suffering might be a part of the Christian life? Why do you think this is (Romans 8:17)?

_____

_____

_____

What does verse 10 say that God will do for us in our suffering?

_____

_____

_____

In my book *Role of a Lifetime,* we are reminded that in every life story there is a villain who wants to win: "He wants to make your life so miserable, so full of fear, confusion, worry, and doubt that you will simply become paralyzed and unable to move forward in any kind of productive and redeeming way. If he can immobilize you, if he can demoralize you, if he can distract you from the role God has cast you in, he will have accomplished his purpose. The one purpose of the enemy is the destruction of all God loves, particularly His beloved. That's you and me."[3]

What has the enemy of your soul done to you lately?

_____

_____

_____

Almighty God, the enemy may taunt and torture me, but by Your strength in my life, he will not win me over! In Christ's name, Amen.

—— DAY 3: GOD OFFERS STRENGTH
Gracious God, today I feel weak, but I thank You that in my weakness, You are strong. In Christ's name, Amen.

Read Psalm 18:1-6. This psalm is a song of deliverance written by King David after the Lord rescued him from his enemies, which included the powerful King Saul (story found in 2 Samuel 22:1-51). According to Bible teacher Debbie Alsdorf, this psalm pictures God in five ways:

1. **God our rock.** He cannot be moved, even by our enemy. Solid and secure are we with God as our rock.
2. **God our fortress.** He is a place of safety.
3. **God our shield.** He is a barrier that comes between us and everything that passes through our life. Some describe this as having a "Father-filtered" life.
4. **God the horn or strength of our salvation.** Our salvation or deliverance doesn't rest on me. It rests on the strength of God; therefore, it is secure.
5. **God our stronghold.** If we need help or provision, we are to look to God. He is the One who holds us with strength that cannot be measured, for He alone is mighty and powerful above all else. We can trust in Him and in His strong grip on our lives.[4]

Which of these pictures of God do you need most on your journey toward health? Why?

_____

_____

_____

Which of these pictures of God gives you most comfort and hope today, and why?

_____

_____

In *That Incredible Christian*, A. W. Tozer reminds us that God wants to give each of His children divine strength to stand against any enemy: "The purest saint at the moment of his greatest strength is as weak as he was before his concession. What has happened is that he has switched from his little human battery to the infinite power of God. He has quite literally exchanged weakness for strength, but the strength is not his, it flows into him from God as long as he abides in Christ."[5]

Have you taken hold of God's strength today? What can you do to plug into that power?

_____

_____

_____

Thank You for being my Stronghold, my Rock and my Fortress today as I stand up against those who would discourage or distract me from knowing my true life's purpose. In Christ's name, Amen.

—— DAY 4: GOD LIFTS AND SUSTAINS
Lord, when I am deep in the pit, please lift me up so that I may move forward with purpose and power. In Christ's name, Amen.

Read Psalm 18:16-19. List the verb phrases that describe what God did for King David:

verse 16: _____

verse 16: _____

verse 16: _____

verse 17: _____

verse 18: _____

verse 19: _____

verse 19: _____

verse 19: _____

Which of these actions do you need God to do in your life today, and why?

_____

_____

_____

Read Psalm 18:30-36, in which David continues to praise God for making him strong. Write down phrases of praise:

verse 30: _____

verse 30: _____
verse 30: _____
verse 31: _____
verse 31: _____
verse 32: _____
verse 32: _____
verse 33: _____
verse 33: _____
verse 34: _____
verse 34: _____
verse 35: _____
verse 35: _____
verse 35: _____
verse 36: _____
verse 36: _____

Did you get all 16 on David's list? Wow!

Now, write your own litany of praise to God, below or in your journal, for how He has helped you thus far in seeking to be healthy in all four areas of your life. For example, "You have helped me drive past fast-food takeout windows without ordering," or "You have wakened me early each morning so I could do my Bible study."

_____
_____
_____
_____
_____
_____

Gracious God, I am amazed and so thankful for new disciplines and activities in my life. Thank You for giving me power. In Christ's name, Amen.

—— DAY 5: GOD GIVES COURAGE

Heavenly Father, may I always trust You to help me when I falter and fail. In Christ's name, Amen.

Read Joshua 1:6-9. What phrase is mentioned three different times in these verses?

_____

_____

_____

Why do you and I need courage? Because fear is alive and well as we pursue balanced health. We have very real fears of what will happen if we don't lose the weight we need to lose, or if we do lose weight, then gain it back again. Personally, I dread failure after so many attempts at change. Do you sometimes struggle with fear? What are you most afraid of?

_____

_____

_____

Carole Lewis suggests that we need constant reminders to live in trust and dependence on God, believing that He will give us courage to fight fear and anxiety. She suggests:

1. Choose to obey God and leave the consequences of life to Him.
2. Recognize that God is greater than your circumstances.
3. Ask God to make you aware of His presence.
4. Praise God for delivering you from your fears.[6]

What specific action will you take to follow through on fighting fear – write down one instance in each of these categories:

Choose to obey God and leave the consequences of life to Him.

_____

_____

_____

Recognize that God is greater than my circumstances.

_____

_____

_____

Ask God to make me aware of His presence.

_____

_____

_____

Praise God for delivering me from my fears.

_____
_____
_____

Carole also notes that as we apply these four steps to our lives and hold them in our hearts, we will be victorious in conquering any obstacle of fear, concerning weight loss or other struggles.

Father, thank You for always standing beside me through whatever comes my way. In Christ's name, Amen.

—— DAY 6: REFLECTION AND APPLICATION
Great are You, Lord, and Your strength makes me strong. Hallelujah! In Christ's name, Amen.

Read Philippians 4:12-13. What sorts of experiences has Paul gone through (v. 12)? Which of these have you also encountered?

_____
_____
_____

Strength is more than firm bodies and toned muscles (although that's important too, and hopefully you're building those). According to Paul, the "secret of being content in every situation" is what (v. 13)?

_____
_____
_____

In what areas are you most discontented?

_____
_____
_____

Does focusing on those areas make you stronger or weaker? Why?

_____
_____
_____

A. W. Tozer once observed, "It is often said that we become like the person we spend the most time with. In fact, we do pick up their mannerisms and values as a part of our relationship with them. The same is true of our relationship with God. The more we spend time with Him the more we become like Him. Perhaps He is leading us to lay aside less important things that take up our time so we could and would spend that time with Him."[7] What do you think God may be calling you to lay aside in order to get to know Him better?

Today, take time with the God of all strength. Soak up His presence. Bask in His love. And echo Paul's words in verse 13: "I can do everything through him who gives me strength."

Heavenly Father, may nothing in this world come before my devotion to and delight in You. In Christ's name, Amen.

—— DAY 7: REFLECTION AND APPLICATION

Master, help me to draw close to You each day so that I will always be prepared for unexpected battles. In Christ's name, Amen.

Since we're studying battle imagery all week, it might be instructive to look at some of the greatest warriors of all time—those from the Roman Empire. The shields of Roman soldiers were 4 feet by 21/2 feet, rectangular, and made of several layers of coated wood. Fiery darts would go into the shields and be put out. Helmets were of bronze; they were very heavy but extremely protective. It is said that during the heyday of the Roman Empire, the soldiers carried out daily maneuvers even in peace time, giving their all so that they would be prepared physically and mentally to withstand battle when it came.

The historian Josephus said, "No confusion breaks their customary formation, no panic paralyzes, no fatigue exhausts them. By their military exercises, the Romans instill into their soldiers fortitude not only of body, but also of soul."[8]
Unfortunately, most historians agree that Rome eventually brought about its own downfall. Edward Gibbon reports that during the reign of Emperor Gratian, these rigorous disciplines were relaxed. Soldiers said the armor was too heavy, so they didn't use their shields and helmets. And because they didn't practice for battle each

day, when the fighting actually came, they were weak and unprepared.[9]

In your battle of life, do you sometimes find the armor burdensome? Does the shield of faith sometimes feel too heavy? Are you tempted to compromise your faith at your workplace, with your social circle, or online? Has your sword dulled from disuse? Are you staying in the Word of God and learning it in your heart so that you can know what God wants and how to live?

As Beth Moore writes, "God has handed us two sticks of dynamite with which to demolish our strongholds: His Word and prayer. What is more powerful than two sticks of dynamite placed in separate locations? Two strapped together. Prayer keeps us in constant communion with God, which is the goal of our entire believing lives."[10] As Christ-followers, we have been equipped with what we need to prevail. No matter what we do, we must remember to hold on to prayer and Bible study as powerful instruments for standing strong!

Spend some time today praying God's Word, "strapping together" the two sticks of powerful dynamite God has provided you. A great place to start is the Psalms, many of which are prayers or testimonies about God's power and care. Find a psalm that speaks into your mind and heart today, and write it in your journal. When you feel attacked or under siege in the next week, use your dynamite! Pray that psalm and stand strong.

Almighty God, I pray today believing You can do what You say, and that is the greatest power in the world. In Christ's name, Amen.

Notes

1. Beth Moore, Praying God's Word (Nashville, TN: B&H Publishers, 2000), p. 3.

2. John Eldredge, Epic (Nashville, TN: Thomas Nelson Publishers, 2004), p. 100.

3. Lucinda Secrest McDowell, Role of a Lifetime: Your Part in God's Story (Nashville, TN: B&H Publishers, 2008)

4. Debbie Alsdorf, Restoring Love (Colorado Springs CO: David C. Cook Publishers, 2001), p. 25.

5. A.W. Tozer, That Incredible Christian (Camp Hill, PA: Christian Publications, 1986), p. 33.

6. Carole Lewis, The Divine Diet (Ventura, CA: Gospel Light Publishers, 2004), p. 195.

7. A.W. Tozer, Gems from Tozer (Camp Hill, PA: Christian Publications, Inc., 1979).

8. Flavius Josephus, The Jewish War, vol. III (Harvard University Press, 1997), p. 27.

9. Edward Gibbon, History of the Decline and Fall of the Roman Empire, vol. III (New York, Harper & Brothers Publishers, 1880), p. 238.

10. Moore, Praying God's Word, p. 6

WEEK FIVE: SEARCH INWARD

SCRIPTURE MEMORY VERSE
Search me, O God, and know my heart; test me and know my anxious thoughts.
See if there is any offensive way in me, and lead me in the way everlasting. **Psalm**
139:23-24

I fought silence for a long time. I knew that solitude and quietness were essential for soul care, but I resisted. Noise and busyness seemed like friends because they engaged me and filled those spaces so I didn't have to face what was going on deep inside. Just keep all the plates spinning, and hope for the best.

But of course, no one can sustain such a life for the long haul. We eventually crash and burn. Or, in my case, we implode and it is not a pretty sight. At some point each of us must come to end of ourselves and face our Maker. What I discovered at my lowest point was that the heart of God toward me was filled with compassion, forgiveness, mercy, and grace. In such a moment we can submit to His will and His way – which first calls us into a focused time in His presence – or we can continue to run our own lives. We can choose life... or death.

In this week's memory verse, King David asks God to enter the depths of his life—his heart—and to reveal his desires, actions, thoughts, habits, beliefs or sin. This is all to one purpose: so that David might choose life and be led to the "way everlasting."

Any true search for God's purpose must include a time of searching inward. That can be really scary! Often, we expend lots of energy covering up and building walls of protection.

There are many coping mechanisms I've used to avoid facing my ugly truth— and emotional eating is one of them. In some weird mixed up way, for me food sometimes offers comfort, love, security, companionship, distraction and a way to avoid confronting what needed to change.

Ouch. Have your toes just been stepped on? Well, if they have, please know this: As we search inward this week, God is already here. He does not want to step on our toes; He wants to heal our hearts.

—— DAY 1: GOD KNOWS ME—INSIDE AND OUT
God, it's a bit gritty inside my heart, but I know that You will help me become clean and changed. In Christ's name, Amen.

Do you believe you can hide from God? We may have everyone else fooled about what we do or who we are, but God—our Creator and Redeemer—simply knows everything about us.

Read Psalm 139:1-4,13-16. What are the things King David observes in verses 1-4 about God and what He knows?

_____

_____

_____

How does it make you feel to acknowledge that God knows all about you?

_____

_____

_____

What thoughts have you had lately that you wish God didn't know? (Write these in your journal if you're concerned about privacy.)

_____

_____

_____

In verses 13-16, we read of God's earliest knowledge of us and our bodies. Write down verse 14 here:

_____

_____

_____

Do you praise God for your body, or are you more likely to blame Him?

_____

_____

_____

What does it mean for you to acknowledge that God ordained all your days before you were even born (v. 16)? (Yes, even those days . . .)

_____

_____

_____

In response to life's wounds, sometimes people turn to behaviors that either release tension or numb pain. We've already mentioned emotional eating as one of those, but there are many other habits, such as gambling, workaholism, explosive anger, substance abuse or sexual impurity, that can become addictive. Pretty soon, such things take on a life of their own and begin to grip us so we can't stop ourselves. Unless we call on God to reveal in the light what we do in the dark, we can never address the root issues and come clean. Hiding such things only increases our shame and prevents the needed healing and hope-giving redemption.

Examine your heart and pray for God to search out what you need to address in your inner soul so that you may walk fully in the light of Christ. Compose your own version of our memory verse here:

_____

_____

_____

Thank You, Lord, for revealing even those hard things about my life, actions and choices. Let's work on them together. In Christ's name, Amen.

—— DAY 2: GOD'S LOVE CHANGES ME
Gracious God, I cringe sometimes when I think of mistakes I have made in the past. Thank You for being willing to love me into a new life. In Christ's name, Amen.

Have you heard that old joke, "The reality check is in the mail . . ."? Reality is sometimes a jolt to the system, but facing the truth of what is going on inside of us is a necessary first step toward any positive change. Because God created us and loves us unconditionally, He wants us to be whole and able to fulfill His purpose. Unfortunately, that usually comes through change, which is hard. But change can also be life giving.

Read Ephesians 2:1-10. In verses 1-3, we see a picture of those who follow the ways of the world and of the enemy of our souls. How does Paul describe that kind of life and behavior?

_____
_____
_____

How would you translate this to describe your behaviors before embarking on your First Place for Health journey?

_____
_____
_____

What did God do and why did He do it (vv. 4-7)?

_____
_____
_____

Write a prayer of thanks to God for His actions on your behalf.

_____
_____
_____

If you fully understand and embrace the meaning in verses 8 and 9, your life will be changed forever. What does it mean to be "saved by grace through faith"?

_____
_____
_____

What do you think Paul means by the phrases "the gift of God" and "so that no one can boast"?

_____
_____
_____

Have you ever tried to earn God's salvation—to be perfect and receive His love as a reward? What was the result?

_____
_____
_____

In my very first book, *Amazed by Grace*, I attempted to explain what I had learned about grace; "Grace is God giving us what we don't deserve; mercy is God not giving us what we do deserve. So, the very nature of grace is that it is undeserved. To show grace is to extend favor to one who doesn't deserve it and can never earn it. But what do we deserve as a result of our sin and efforts to take God's place as controller of our lives? We deserve judgment and punishment. That's where both mercy and grace come in—God in His infinite mercy does not give us the death we deserve, but as an act of grace grants us forgiveness and new life."[1]

That forgiveness and new life come when we place our faith in Him. Have you ever thought your works would get you into heaven (v. 9)? If so, what do you believe now?

_____
_____
_____

It is important to note that while our works don't earn us God's love, we are created for good works as a response to the love God has granted us as His children. As you read verse 10, write down ways you have been loved, forgiven and changed.

_____
_____
_____

What are some of the works you believe God has created you to do?

_____
_____
_____

Okay, Lord, I give up. I'm going to stop striving right now and rest in Your life-changing gifts of grace and mercy from now on. In Christ's name, Amen.

—— DAY 3: CONSEQUENCES OF BAD CHOICES
Heavenly Father, I tried it my way and things got worse. I'm going to do it Your way from now on. In Christ's name, Amen.

I may or may not have quipped this at one time or another: "If I eat this cookie standing up (or in my bedroom or while driving), the calories don't count"! How ridiculous that sounds, and yet I've discovered when recording my daily intake on the Live It

Tracker that I too easily fall prey to a number of "lurking nibbles," while cooking, cleaning up, serving kids, and so on. My choices produce consequences. Good choices produce good results. Poor choices bring heartache and often failure.

Paul reminds the Galatians that "we reap what we sow." Read Galatians 6:7-8. Write down the life lesson revealed in verse 8.

The one who sows to please his sinful nature will reap _____.
The one who sows to please the Spirit will reap _____.

Even though we know this life lesson is true, there seem to be little triggers causing us to occasionally follow the path away from health and wholeness. When you have turned the wrong way in the past week, what triggered that action?

_____

_____

_____

Do you remember a few years ago when singer Mandisa was a contestant on American Idol? Many of us were shocked when she was mocked by judge Simon Cowell due to her weight: "I think we're going to need a bigger stage." After forgiving him and testifying on network television, she was then voted off the reality show. Her health challenges had played out in public for everyone to see, and the ensuing letdown caused Mandisa to cry out to God:

> "I was standing up for You, and I was on that stage trying to proclaim how good You are. How could You let this happen to me? I dealt with my anger by eating: pizza, fast food, entire pies, Krispy Kreme donuts. I ate just about everything imaginable, and I was miserable. I was in the biggest pit of my life, and I shut everybody out. I turned the ringer off my phone. I didn't talk to the Lord."[2]

Fortunately, in the midst of this spiritual and emotional wilderness, God's unconditional love broke through to Mandisa and began a healing in her heart, which also jumpstarted a physical improvement and an 80-pound weight loss. Isn't it interesting to note that heart healing and body healing often go hand in hand? Mandisa continues:

> "I wish I'd sought God and turned to His Word and not shut out everybody who loves me and could have spoken godly wisdom into my life. I eventually learned the power of praising God when you don't feel like it. I think that's the most important

time to worship the Lord because when you magnify Him, your problems look smaller by comparison. If I'd done that, I don't think I would have gotten into that pit. The next difficult situation I face, I'll know to turn to God, to look for His lessons and higher purposes and redemption."[3]

When one of your triggers threatens to turn you down the wrong path in the coming week, what are two things you can do to "turn to God, to look for His lessons and higher purposes and redemption"?

_____

_____

_____

Thank You for continuing to put people in my path who help to turn me back to You and who speak truth into my soul. In Christ's name, Amen.

—— DAY 4: HIDDEN THOUGHTS
Dear Heavenly Father, I know that You search my motives and my desires, and I ask that You would help me to grow today in godliness. In Christ's name, Amen.

As I ask God to look within me, I pray for the mind of Christ. Most battles begin and end in the mind—the body and actions simply follow our intellectual choices. Have you asked God to search your thoughts? Are you enslaved to negativity or a spirit of defeat?

_____

_____

_____

_____

_____

Read 1 Corinthians 2:10-16. In verses 10-12, how does Paul say that we can know the thoughts of God?

_____

_____

_____

_____

_____

In verses 13-16, we read about spiritual understanding on a deep level. How do you feel that God is granting you more discernment as you make daily choices to obey His Spirit?

_____

_____

_____

What practices can you do to help you keep your thoughts pure, positive and prayerful?

_____

_____

_____

When I was in college, I was privileged to meet Corrie ten Boom. Her Christian family hid Jews in their Dutch home during World War II and were sent to concentration camps in punishment. Her family died, but Corrie emerged at the end of the war, vowing to be a "tramp for the Lord" and travel all over the world speaking of God's faithfulness and the power of forgiveness. Yet even this godly woman knew about the struggle with sin:

> "If we look within ourselves we are bound to find more and more sin. Why not pray with the psalmist, "Search me, O God, and know my heart." He will show you your sins. Not all of them at once, but increasingly you will recognize them, and always in the light of Christ's finished work upon the cross. Then God makes it very clear where you have to make restitution, and so you get right with God and right with men. To the end of our lives it remains a struggle against sin, but a victorious struggle. If only we put on the whole armor of God we go from victory to victory."[4]

As God shows you the depths of your heart, are you discovering areas that need to be made right? What do you need to "get right with God and right with men"?

_____

_____

_____

From whom do you need forgiveness today? How will that happen?

_____

_____

_____

Thank You, Lord, for giving me a mind that can think and reason and make godly choices. In Christ's name, Amen.

—— DAY 5: ENTER GOD'S PRESENCE

Lord, I come to You now and seek Your guidance and grace for all that is ahead of me on this new day. In Christ's name, Amen.

Read Hebrews 10:19-25. The best way to grow in spirit is to consciously enter into God's presence on an ongoing daily basis. How are we to draw near to God (v. 22)?

_____

_____

_____

Which of these is hardest for you to do?

_____

_____

_____

In God's presence, we're encouraged to do four important things (vv. 23- 25). List them here:

Let us _____

Let us _____

Let us _____

Let us _____

Someone once said we literally "spend" our lives, in a way similar to spending money. Like a bank account, if we take continual withdrawals and don't make deposits, we quickly become overdrawn. Author Nancie Carmichael laments, "Over the years, I had not made the necessary 'deposits'—I had been running in the red, emotionally and physically for too long. The needs seemed so great, never ending. And yet I missed a step—unless I received spiritual nourishment, there was no way I could continue to 'feed' others."[5]

Review the four activities we should engage in while in God's presence (vv. 23-25), and then write down one specific way you will pursue each one this week:

Hold on to hope _____

Spur one another _____

Meet together _____

Encourage one another _____

Gracious God, guide me to someone today who needs encouragement and a word from You. In Christ's name, Amen.

—— DAY 6: REFLECTION AND APPLICATION

Father, I want to be beautiful, both inside and out. Please help me to work on both in a balanced manner. In Christ's name, Amen.

Read 1 Peter 3:3-4. As this week's study draws to a close, let's look at beauty—specifically, *inner* beauty. People today still mock inner beauty as though it were a poor runner-up to outer beauty. In fact, there was even a reality television show based on that premise. Yet God (the One who thought up beauty in the first place!) says that inner beauty is the winner, not the consolation prize. This passage from Peter states what is of great worth in God's sight. Describe that beauty (v. 4).

_____

_____

_____

Do you know people with a gentle and quiet spirit? How does being in their presence make you feel?

_____

_____

_____

What do you think you'd have to do to display those qualities?

_____

_____

_____

Read 1 Samuel 16:7. In this story, God tells Samuel, who is searching for Israel's next king, how His ways are in contrast to the world's ways. How do you formulate a first impression of someone? What do you notice first?

_____
_____
_____

When evaluating a person, what does God see first and foremost?

_____
_____
_____

What our culture values is displayed at every turn in the media, advertisements, celebrities and pop culture. But these are faulty mirrors. When we look into them, all they point out is what we lack. In order to move into wholeness and discover God's purpose for our lives, we need to consult different mirrors: reflections of what God says is true and holy through His Word, the Bible.

Who are two or three godly men or women who will be models to you of beauty?

_____
_____
_____

God, give me a beautiful heart and may that be visible to all around me. In Christ's name, Amen.

—— DAY 7: REFLECTION AND APPLICATION
Lord, help me to incorporate spiritual disciplines into my life so that I may stay close to You and grow in godliness. In Christ's name, Amen.

Read Psalm 25:4-6. Use this Scripture to offer a prayer of petition to God:

Show me _____
Teach me _____
Guide me _____
Teach me _____
My hope _____
Remember _____

Try to take an extra amount of time to be quiet before God today. Solitude and sanctuary are important aspects of our spiritual lives, yet are often neglected due to constant demands from others. Get in the habit of scheduling time for Sabbath rest, preferably on a Sunday. As Dallas Willard states:

> My central claim is that we can become like Christ by doing one thing—by following Him in the overall style of life He chose for Himself. If we have faith in Christ, we must believe that He knew how to live. We can, through faith and grace, become like Christ by practicing the types of activities He engaged in by arranging our whole lives around the activities He Himself practiced in order to remain constantly at home in the fellowship of His Father. What activities did Jesus practice? Such things as solitude and silence, prayer, simple and sacrificial living, intense study and meditation upon God's Word and God's ways, and service to others. Some of them will certainly be even more necessary to us than they were to Him, because of our greater or different need.

> So, if we wish to follow Christ—and to walk in the easy yoke with Him—we will have to accept His overall way of life as our way of life totally. Then, and only then, we may reasonably expect to know by experience how easy is the yoke and how light the burden.[6]

What are three spiritual disciplines you will incorporate into your journey with God?

_____

_____

_____

Almighty God, may I seek regular times for solitude and silence even though that goes against my nature. In Christ's name, Amen.

Notes

1. Lucinda Secrest McDowell, Amazed by Grace (Bolivar, MO: Quiet Waters Publica- tions, 2002), p. 23.
2. Camerin Courtney, "TCW Talks to Mandisa," Today's Christian Woman, July/August 2009, p. 19.
3. Ibid.
4. Corrie Ten Boom, Not Good If Detached (Fort Washington, PA: Christian Literature Crusade, 1957), p. 108.
5. Nancie Carmichael, Praying for Rain (Nashville, TN: Thomas Nelson Publishers, 2001), p. 61.
6. Dallas Willard, Spirit of the Disciplines: Understanding How God Changes Lives (San Fran- cisco, CA: Harper and Row, 1988), p. 8.

WEEK SIX: OVERCOME CHALLENGES

SCRIPTURE MEMORY VERSE
Everyone born of God overcomes the world. This is the victory that has overcome the world, even our faith. Who is it that overcomes the world? Only he who believes that Jesus is the Son of God. 1 John 5:4-5

My eldest son is an overcomer. Born with intellectual disabilities, he has faced many challenges in life, especially in certain areas like reading, writing, and understanding nuance. But he makes up for that in sheer determination and a vibrant faith that whatever God calls him to do, God will provide! And, he never stops talking.

When Justin was little and people would ask me what kind of future I thought he could have, I wearily-but-hopefully replied, "We are just taking it one day at a time" as I continued to read to him daily and teach him all the life skills I taught our other three children. And do you know what, thirty-seven years later this young man lives in his own apartment, has worked at Red Lobster for two decades, won countless gold medals for Special Olympics tennis, and is volunteering at the church every time the doors are open. Both of his sisters asked him to read Scripture in their weddings and his current favorite role is Uncle Justin to a niece and three nephews.

What do you think of when you hear a person referred to as an "overcomer"? Chances are, you're reminded of someone who has faced major obstacles or catastrophic challenges, yet has persevered and been successful, prevailing against all odds.

According to verse 5 of our memory verse, who is an overcomer?

Are you born of God? Do you believe that Jesus is the Son of God? If so, are you an overcomer?

Write down the challenges that you are facing this week that you desire to overcome.

_____

_____

_____

—— DAY 1: STRUGGLING INSIDE

*Almighty God, this whole balanced life thing is a lot harder than I thought, so I'm glad
You're not giving up on me. In Christ's name, Amen.*

Sometimes I am my own worst enemy. I struggle against myself and my will. I know
what to do, yet too often I don't do it. When was the last time you experienced such
an inner struggle?

_____

_____

_____

Read Romans 7:14-25. Does it surprise you that even the apostle Paul wrestled in a
similar way? What does Paul confess in verse 15?

_____

_____

_____

What does he identify as the source of his struggle (vv. 17-20)?

_____

_____

_____

What basic conclusion does he reach in verse 21?

_____

_____

_____

Verses 22 and 23 describe how we can know what God wants—and even want what
God wants—but still do the opposite. What is Paul's explanation for this behavior?

_____

_____

_____

How are your body's desires at odds with your spirit's desires?

Write down where you can find rescue (v. 25).

Joanna Weaver, author of *Having a Mary Spirit*, refers to the struggles Paul mentions as her battle with the part of herself she calls "Flesh Woman":

> Flesh Woman is that contrary, rebellious, incredibly self-centered version of you who shows up when things don't go the way you planned and life seems habitually unfair. [She's the] righteous indignation we use to justify our not-so-righteous anger. The flattery we pour on in order to secure coveted positions. The false humility in which we cloak ourselves while secretly hoping to be admired. Unfortunately, we rarely pause to wonder if what we're doing is wrong. And that's just where Flesh Woman wants it to be. For if you were to pull off her mask, you'd know what she's really up to. Her main goal is not your benefit, but her power base. Though Flesh Woman would never admit it, she's determined to do whatever it takes to remain in control of your life.[1]

Do you feel imprisoned by "Flesh Woman" or "Flesh Man"? Write a prayer, asking God to free you to obey Him.

Thank You, Lord, that You are in control and You will help me to be an overcomer. In Christ's name, Amen.

—— DAY 2: GOD'S COMFORT
Heavenly Father, Your presence and peace in the midst of my pain are a great comfort to me. In Christ's name, Amen.

It's hard to be in the middle of a fight for your life, isn't it? And yet, that's just what we feel like sometimes—that we are struggling just to keep our heads above water. One way that God enables us to become overcomers is through His presence and power. When Jesus calls the Holy Spirit "the Comforter," He is saying that the Spirit is our strength—His strength is what brings comfort to us. The word "comforter" as applied to the Holy Spirit in the original Greek is *paracleto*, which means "helper," "advocate" and "strengthener." Christ promised that this Strengthener would be with us forever.

Read 2 Corinthians 1:3-6. What names does Paul call God in verse 3?

_____

_____

_____

What does God do for us, and why does He do it (v. 4)?

_____

_____

_____

Paul said two related things flow over our lives. What are they (v. 5)?

_____

_____

What does God's comfort achieve for a person who is seeking to be an overcomer (v. 6)?

_____

_____

_____

Today is a good day to extend comfort to someone who needs it. Think of ways others have comforted you, and do the same to comfort someone else today. Who? Ask God to reveal a name to you as you go through your prayer list, read your church bulletin or even drive in your neighborhood. As you serve, you may find yourself comforted in the process.

Dearest Jesus, help me know who to comfort today and give me the boldness to reach out to them in Your name. In Christ's name, Amen.

—— DAY 3: ADOPTED BY GOD

Abba, thank You for adopting me into Your family so that I don't have to live as an orphan anymore. In Christ's name, Amen.

I will never forget that beautiful summer day in Seattle when I walked into a court room and walked out as the adoptive mother of two sons and a daughter. I wore a corsage, we took pictures, and sent out engraved announcements joyfully stating "Here am I and the children God has given me!" Isaiah 8:18 Ever since that time, I have held a new and deeper understanding of what God has done in adopting us into His forever family. Read Romans 8:9-17. According to verses 15-17, what does it mean to be adopted by God?

_____

_____

_____

After participating in several adoptions, one Seattle attorney said, "I have begun to see in the lives of the adoptive families I work with a picture of God's love—for others and for me. I have concluded that recovering a biblical theology of adoption can help us know more about God and experience Him in new and vital ways."[2]

In verses 9-13, Paul reminds the Romans that they are controlled by the Spirit living in them. Write down each reference to what the Spirit does in those five verses.

_____

_____

_____

What is the end result? (The last three words of verse 13 have the answer.)

_____

_____

_____

In verse 14, Paul introduces a revolutionary concept that those who are led by the Spirit are of God. What does that mean for us as it relates to fear (v. 15)?

_____

_____

_____

Abba is the Aramaic term for "Daddy." By suggesting that believers call the Creator of the Universe "Daddy," Paul is proposing a radical acknowledgment of intimate relationship with Him.

Do you live in a "spirit of fear" or a "spirit of sonship" when it comes to your relationship to God? Explain.

_____
_____
_____

When someone chooses to adopt a son or a daughter, a legal contract provides for a brand-new birth certificate, which states their relationship as parent and child from now on. That's a picture of what happened when we chose to become Christ-followers. How is this reality confirmed (v. 16)?

_____
_____
_____

And what will be the outcome (v. 17)?

_____
_____
_____

Write a prayer to your heavenly Father, sharing your feelings about being His adopted son or daughter.

Dear Abba,

_____
_____
_____
_____
_____
_____
_____

Love, Your son/daughter,

I promise, heavenly Father, to live from now on as a daughter/son of the King of kings and Lord of lords! In Christ's name, Amen.

—— DAY 4: MORE THAN CONQUERORS

Dear God, Your followers can do this together—we can conquer anything that comes our way and threatens to keep us from Your purpose. Amen.

More than conquerors. This was the theme I was invited to speak on at an annual banquet in Boston for the Joni and Friends ministry to those with disabilities. Joni Eareckson Tada was only 17 years old when she dove into a shallow pool and emerged a quadriplegic. Faced with numerous opportunities to give up in defeat, Joni has instead fought valiantly for more than 50 years—not only for her own life's meaning and ministry, but for the rights and the quality of both physical and spiritual lives of countless unnamed others who struggle against tremendous odds through their disabilities.

Joni would likely be the first to echo the apostle Paul: "No, in all these things we are more than conquerors through Him who loved us." We can all be overcomers if we realize that even in hard times, God is conforming us to His image.

Read Romans 8:35-39. Name seven specific things that might threaten to separate you from Christ's love (v. 35).

1. _____
2. _____
3. _____
4. _____
5. _____
6. _____
7. _____

Can they? Write down verse 37 as your answer.

_____
_____
_____

In verses 38 and 39, Paul lists 10 more things that cannot separate us from Christ's love. List them here:

1. _____
2. _____
3. _____
4. _____
5. _____
6. _____

7. _____
8. _____
9. _____
10. _____

Joni Eareckson Tada says, "Sometimes God will use suffering and affliction to sandblast us to the core and get us seriously thinking about larger than life issues of heaven and hell. I just don't know that we would think about these issues if it were not for an ice-cold splash of suffering waking us out of our spiritual slumber. God's purpose in redeeming us is not to make our lives happy, healthy and free of trouble. It is not an escape from our physical pains. His purpose is to make us more like Christ. He will choose to allow spinal cord injury or multiple sclerosis or blindness or stroke or Alzheimer's or whatever to not only teach us, but also our loved ones, about what it means to become more like Him." What is God using in your life to teach you "what it means to become more like Him?"

_____
_____
_____

Thank You, Lord, that literally nothing that comes my way can ever come between You and me—I'm counting on it! In Christ's name, Amen.

—— DAY 5: WORTHY WEAPONS
Almighty God, may I be brave and wise enough to use the weapons You have provided as I seek to change my life. In Christ's name, Amen.

Read 2 Corinthians 10:1-6. Those of us who desire to become spiritual overcomers must realize that we do not live by the same standards as the world. In these verses, Paul contrasts "the world" with the life of a believer in several ways (vv. 3-4). Explain what he means in your own words.

_____
_____
_____

What are three ways we use God's weapons (vv. 5-6)?

_____
_____
_____

One of the most important weapons in our arsenal is prayer. In fact, the Lord's Prayer ends with the plea for God to "deliver us from evil." And since there's evil around us at every turn, it's a good idea to pray the Lord's Prayer every single day! Prayer is a weapon that demolishes strongholds. If you are dealing with strongholds in your life (and who isn't?), perhaps the following prayer from Peter Scazzero's book *Daily Office* will help:

> Lord, You are right that I have a powerful demonic enemy seeking to lure me into a pit and dominate me. Snatch me from the evil one! Rescue me from Satan's desire to destroy my faith. Help me discern the temptations of Satan coming at me. Teach me to wait on You when tempted in the wilderness, like Jesus. I place my confidence in You, Father, to care for me today. You speak the truth when You say: "The one who is in you is greater than the one who is in the world" (1 John 4:4). So I affirm with King David: "I will not fear the tens of thousands drawn up against me on every side" (Psalm 3:6). You are good and Your love endures forever. Amen.[3]

When I am weak, Lord, You are strong. When I am afraid, Lord, You are brave for me. Thank You. In Christ's name, Amen.

—— DAY 6: REFLECTION AND APPLICATION

Dear God of a thousand new beginnings, I'm grateful that You have offered me a fresh start at a life that is healthier on all levels. Amen.

Read 2 Corinthians 5:16-21. What does verse 17 mean to you, for your life?

_____

_____

_____

Look up the meaning of the word "reconciliation" and write it here:

_____

_____

_____

What do you think Paul means when he writes of reconciliation in the following verses?

Reconciling us to God through Christ (v. 18):

_____

_____

_____

Giving us ministry of reconciliation (v. 18):

_____

_____

_____

God reconciling the world to Himself (v. 19):

_____

_____

_____

Committing us to the ministry of reconciliation (v. 19):

_____

_____

_____

Be reconciled to God (v. 20):

_____

_____

_____

Do you see yourself as "Christ's ambassador" to the world (v. 20)? How are you carrying out that role?

_____

_____

_____

If God's Son, Jesus, was perfect and sinless, why did He die on the cross (v. 21)?

_____

_____

_____

If Jesus paid that ultimate price—death for our sins—then how do you think we should respond to Him, in our lives (v. 21)?

_____

_____

_____

Sometimes it's hard to think of myself as righteous. But I find it easier to think of myself as new. In this newness of life, you and I can both seek to live in a way that glorifies God and that seeks holiness.

Lord, sometimes when we're new, we don't always know how to act and what to do, but we thank You that You will show us the new path. Amen.

—— DAY 7: REFLECTION AND APPLICATION

Lord, give me a new vision of the balanced life You have for me, which will come as I follow Your will and Your way. As I embrace Your law, may I also rejoice in the blessing. In Christ's name, Amen

THE MESSAGE paraphrase of Proverbs 29:18 is, "If people can't see what God is doing, they stumble all over themselves."

I admit that for many years, in desperation, I would eagerly try the "diet of the day," only to toss it aside the moment things got hard. No wonder nothing worked for me. How about you? Do you occasionally stumble around and then just give up—or give in to whatever feels good? Because sometimes eating just feels good. It is familiar and comforting. It numbs us to other things going on in our lives that we aren't ready to address or conquer. But ultimately, overeating or consistent unhealthy eating can lead to a cycle of shame, guilt and defeat.

In my own discouragement, I found myself calling out for help to God, just as the psalmist does. Psalm 73 speaks to those of us caught in a vicious cycle of destruction. Will you cry out to God today? Turn to Psalm 73 and write verses 21-22 below.

_____

_____

_____

God gives four distinct promises to you in Psalm 73:23-24:

He promises to always be _____.
He promises to hold you _____.
He promises to guide you _____.
He promises to take you _____.

Proverbs 20:18 tells us to do something when we make plans. Why do you think this is important?

_____
_____
_____

As you read Psalm 73:23-26, write out phrases that you can remember to claim on your journey toward health and wholeness.

_____
_____
_____

Father, thank You for never giving up on me, even when I have failed. Thank You for promises that remind me You are enough. Amen.

Notes
1. Joanna Weaver, Having a Mary Spirit (Colorado Springs, CO: WaterBrook, 2006), p. 12.
2. David V. Andersen, "When God Adopts," Christianity Today, July 9, 1993, p. 36.
3. Peter Scazzero, Daily Office (Elmhurst, NY: Emotionally Healthy Spirituality, 2008), p. 163.

WEEK SEVEN: RESPOND FAITHFULLY

SCRIPTURE MEMORY VERSE
Whether you turn to the right or to the left, your ears will hear a voice behind you, saying, "This is the way; walk in it." Isaiah 30:21

Do you remember back in the day when everyone first began getting a GPS for our cars? Global Positioning Systems were invented for those of us who are directionally impaired. All I had to do was program an address, stick the small unit on the dashboard, and then follow the GPS's voice instructions directly to my destination!

But first we had to choose a voice. There were at least four options: American accented male or female, or British accented male or female. My husband decided our GPS would use the British female voice and promptly named "her" **G**uinevere **P**enelope **S**imonington (GPS). He had obviously been watching way too much Masterpiece Theatre...

From then on, whatever Guinevere Penelope said in that hoity-toity voice, Mike did to the nth degree. Except that sometimes, Guinevere Penelope gave instructions that were a wee bit off the mark. When that happened, Mike would go his own way, giving GPS time to reconfigure and catch up with him. Once I simply couldn't hold my tongue any longer and wryly observed, "So, what good is it to have GPS if you still have to figure out whether or not to do what she says?"

Exactly. Either we listen to the voice and obey, or we listen to the voice, think about what we want to do on our own and obey only as we see fit. Sometimes obedience suits us, sometimes not.

I admit I'm a bit like that with God. On one hand, I certainly want Him to give me explicit directions and guidance in all things. But sometimes I'm convinced that what He says must be a little "off," so I decide to go my way after all and let Him catch up, "recalculating" all the while . . .

This week we are going to learn how to respond faithfully to God's Voice.

—— DAY 1: GOD ANSWERS

Father, please help me to hear Your voice and Your answer amidst the cacophony of the world today. In Christ's name, Amen.

Read Isaiah 30:1-23. Isaiah 30 is an entire chapter about how God keeps telling Israel what they need to do in order to be delivered from their enemies. But they simply do not want to hear and obey—they continue to wallow in the consequences of their actions. These "chosen people" have rebelled against God and sought negotiations with Egypt. But even though they have turned away, God still doesn't give up on them.

What three items of good news does Isaiah give the Israelites in verse 19?
1. _____
2. _____
3. _____

List the two negatives and two positives found in verse 20.

_____
_____
_____

Think about your life recently and write down some experiences of:

The bread of adversity

_____
_____
_____

The water of affliction

_____
_____
_____

When God's voice makes your path clear (as stated in verse 21), what should be your response? Follow the Israelites' example in verse 22 to guide you in thinking of specific actions to take. What could be some modern-day equivalents to their response to God?

_____
_____
_____

Has anything or anyone become an idol in your life? Explain.

_____

_____

_____

Verse 23 elaborates further on God's gracious provision. What does this mean to you in your present circumstances?

_____

_____

_____

Gracious God, I know I need to lay down all the idols that have taken precedence over You in my life. Today I name them before You and leave them at your feet. In Christ's name, Amen.

—— DAY 2: EARS WIDE OPEN

Father, I'm going to try to speak less and listen more today. Starting now. In Christ's name, Amen.

Yes, it's true that God gave us two ears and only one mouth for a reason. And yet, some days my mouth is open far more often than my ears. In order to truly listen to God's voice, we must have our ears and our heart wide open.

Read Proverbs 23:12. What is King Solomon's advice?

_____

_____

_____

Name one instruction you have received recently in your First Place for Health group that you need to apply to your heart.

_____

_____

_____

British professor and author C. S. Lewis once referred to pain as "God's megaphone." Sometimes God has to shout at us to get our attention. And, sometimes, pain is the very thing that does it.

When Billy and Ruth Graham's home was being built in Montreat, North Carolina, Ruth was on the construction site speaking with one of the carpenters. Engrossed in conversation, she leaned against a piece of equipment and promptly heard a harsh shout from another worker. As she recoiled, he apologized, "I'm so sorry, Mrs. Graham, but you were about to lose your fingers!" Ruth had been leaning next to a moving saw blade. She wisely observed, "I will always be grateful to that man for yelling at me."

Has God "yelled" at you lately? Write down a time when an experience of pain or suffering redirected your attention back to God and spiritual matters.

_____

_____

_____

Did that incident force you to turn to God more and listen to His voice, or did you return to your former ways once the crisis was past?

_____

_____

_____

Gracious God, I didn't much like it when You "shouted" at me through that hard experience, but it did teach me something. Thank You. Amen.

—— DAY 3: OTHER LOUD VOICES

Father, I've had all kinds of videotapes playing in my mind for years and ask You to erase them so I can hear and see the truth from You. Amen

As you consider your own wellness journey, what voice rings the loudest in your ears?

_____

_____

_____

In her book *Who Calls Me Beautiful?* Regina Franklin urges the wisdom of identifying the "other voices" that speak into our lives:

We must learn to identify the words spoken by the one who seeks to destroy our souls. Satan is a liar. Deception is at the core of his being. We must identify his words when we hear them— words of rejection, hatred, failure and discontent:

"I'll never measure up."
"I can never be beautiful."
"If I were prettier, people would love me." "I'm not good at anything."
"If I had new clothes, I'd be satisfied with the way I look." "I'm so fat."

All lies. Words of death, not life. If he can convince us that we're worthless, he can immobilize us and keep us from fulfilling God's plan in our lives. Out of fear of rejection we won't reach out to others. We'll wallow in self-hatred. Out of fear of failure, we won't follow our dreams. We'll drown in discontent.[1]

Yesterday's reading suggested that we apply our ears to knowledge—but that can be easier said than done. Today there are numerous voices that tickle our ears on any subject. You can probably find an argument that defends just about any course of action. You can definitely find countless diets and get-thin-quick schemes. Everyone has a gimmick and an angle. So how do you know which voice is true?

Read Isaiah 8:19-23. Isaiah addresses this very dilemma in verses 19-20. What does he say to do?

_____
_____
_____

What is the penalty for heeding the wrong voices (vv. 21-22)?

_____
_____
_____

Have you ever lashed out at God after you listened to the wrong voices and got burned?

_____
_____
_____

In his book *Emotionally Healthy Spirituality*, Pastor Peter Scazzero states that voices of the surrounding world and our pasts often repeat the deeply held negative beliefs we may have learned in our families and cultures growing up, such as:

- O I am a mistake.
- O I am a burden.
- O I am stupid.
- O I am worthless.
- O I am not allowed to make mistakes.
- O I must be approved by certain people to feel okay.
- O I don't have the right to experience joy and pleasure.
- O I don't have the right to assert myself and say what I think and feel.
- O I don't have a right to feel.
- O I am valued based on my intelligence, wealth, and what I do, not for who I am.[2]

Put a check by any of these negative phrases that have ever reflected your own beliefs, and then explain why you checked those here:

_____
_____
_____

Peter Scazzero goes on to state that if we can embrace the fact that we are unconditionally loved by God, we can instead embrace a more biblical self-understanding as reflected in these statements:

- O I hold myself in high regard despite my imperfections and limits.
- O I am worthy to assert my God-given power in the world.
- O I am entitled to exist.
- O It is good that I exist.
- O I have my own identity from God that is distinct and unique.
- O I am worthy of being valued and paid attention to.
- O I am entitled to joy and pleasure.
- O I am entitled to make mistakes and not be perfect.[3]

Put a check by at least three of these positive phrases that you want to embrace in your life this week. Explain why you're choosing those three here:

_____
_____
_____

Help me, heavenly Father, to remember that Your voice is the One who speaks truth into my life and all others must be carefully screened through Your Word. In Christ's name, Amen.

—— DAY 4: LISTEN UP!

Lord, You know that I would often rather give advice than take it, but I'm trying hard to change and I appreciate You helping me do just that. In Christ's name, Amen.

Do you like to take advice? Or are you one of those folks who love to dole out opinions to others, but rarely heeds the advice someone offers you? King Solomon (the wisest man in the world, by the way) equates wisdom with listening to advice in both Proverbs 12 and 13.

According to Proverbs 12:15, what is the difference between a fool and a wise person?

_____

_____

_____

_____

To whom do you most often go for advice? What is usually the outcome?

_____

_____

_____

_____

Read Proverbs 13:10. Do you think pride plays a part in your decision whether or not to take godly counsel? What are the consequences of pride, according to this verse?

_____

_____

_____

_____

What factors do you use to determine whose advice to heed?

_____

_____

_____

_____

In *The Echo Within*, author Robert Benson advises:

> Sometimes people hesitate to give God any credit for being able to work through the ordinary of our lives, through the very sentences we hear and say. Such touchstone sentences are affirmations, not commands; they illumine rather than instruct. They help you get your bearings, but they do not offer marching orders. They do not say where you are going next as much as they reinforce the direction in which you are heading. To the degree they point you toward a new road, it will most always be a new road with which you are already familiar.[4]

In what "ordinary ways" is God speaking into your life this week?

_____
_____
_____

Thank You, Father, for using good voices of truth to help guide me and show me Your purpose for my life. In Christ's name, Amen.

—— DAY 5: GOD SPEAKS THROUGH HIS WORD
Gracious God, thank You for the Bible and the way it is coming alive as I seek to know what You mean through Your Word. In Christ's name, Amen.

Read 2 Timothy 3:16. What do you think Paul means when he writes that all Scripture is "God-breathed"?

_____
_____
_____

If the Bible is truly God's Word, how does it seek to "speak" to each one of us?

_____
_____
_____

Briefly describe your relationship with your Bible before you began working through *God's Purpose for You*.

_____
_____
_____

And now? What, if anything, has changed?

_____

_____

_____

The divinely inspired Scripture is useful for what four practices?

1. _____

2. _____

3. _____

4. _____

Even after losing weight, Christian singer Mandisa admits that battling food addiction is the most difficult part of her weight-loss journey. Here's another story from her about how knowing Scripture guides her spiritual journey:

> "I'm learning to replace the negative messages I picked up about my body with the truth of God's Word and what He says about me: that He loves me unconditionally and that I'm fearfully and wonderfully made. But since I've been dealing with this addiction for 20 years, I'm not going to retrain my mind overnight. But thankfully God's Word is powerful. I've memorized a lot of scripture, and I've written many more verses on note cards. I used to travel with Beth Moore on her praise team and she'd always say that on the eighth day God created note cards. She'd put scripture prayers on those cards, and now that's what I do. They're with me all the time.[5]

What are three things you can do to become more familiar with your own Bible?

_____

_____

_____

Almighty God, I remembered my verse today and it was just what I needed to know for the moment. Thanks. In Christ's name, Amen.

—— DAY 6: REFLECTION AND APPLICATION

Thank You, Lord, for coming into my heart and living within me so that I might be able to do far more than I ever could have done alone. Amen.

Read Philippians 2:12-18. God's purpose is stated clearly in the first part of verse 16. Write it here:

_____

_____

_____

In order to "hold out" or share the "word of life" better, we must have God living inside us. What great promise can we count on (v. 13)?

_____

_____

_____

What does God call us to continue to do (vv. 12 and 14)

_____

_____

_____

When you complain or argue with others—or even God—what is it usually about?

_____

_____

_____

When you abstain from complaining and arguing, what godly qualities result in your life (v. 15)?

_____

_____

_____

If we are faithful to the God who is faithful to us, what two things should characterize our lives (v. 18)?

1. _____

2. _____

What are several things for which you can rejoice?

_____

_____

_____

Gracious Provider of all things, may I always have a thankful heart for the many blessings You have sent my way. In Christ's name, Amen.

—— DAY 7: REFLECTION AND APPLICATION
Dear God, You truly take me by Your hand and show me the path of life, and I praise You forever! In Christ's name, Amen.

We can rest in God's truth. Read Psalm 16:7-11 – a passage for you to use as a catalyst for praise and prayer to the God who speaks and "makes known to [you] the path of life." There are two particular things that God does, for which the psalmist gives praise in verse 7. What are they?

One of the hard but good truths in life is that people are created with limits. But our bodies can "rest secure" (v. 9). We have limits, but our God is unlimited! Write some of the benefits we receive from this limitless God. Use today's verses for inspiration.

I learned so much from medical doctor Richard Swenson about how people (including believers) must deal with overload.

> Since God is the author and creator of my limits, then it's probably okay with Him that I have limits. He probably does not expect me to be infinite and is a little surprised when I try. It is okay with Him if I am not all things to all people all the time all by myself. As a matter of fact, it is probably not okay with Him if I assume otherwise.
> - You see, it's okay for me to have limits—God doesn't.
> - It is okay for me to get a good night's sleep—God doesn't sleep.
> - It is okay for me to rest—God doesn't need to.
> - It is probably even okay to be depressed—because God isn't. We do not know a lot about what heaven looks like, but this much we know: God is not pacing the throne room anxious and depressed because of the condition of the world. He knows, He is not surprised, and He is sovereign.

• It's okay if we have limits. He is able. Limits were God's intention from the beginning. He decided early on that limits were not only good but necessary. It was His way of preempting any ambiguity about who is God and who is not. He is the Creator—the One without limits. We are the created—the ones with limits. As the author of limits, God put them within us for our protection. We violate them at our peril.[6]

Are there areas in your life where you are attempting to live beyond your limits? How will you begin to practice "letting go and letting God"?

_____

_____

_____

Today your assignment is to listen to God. Focus on being quiet in solitude and in expectation that you will hear from the Lover of your soul. Take a blank notebook or journal with you and write down what you hear God saying to you. (You can write down your prayers/thoughts to Him as well.) Follow the advice of this wise older Christian:

Years ago I learned to read a chapter in the Bible daily and journal about what I read. Now I also ask, "Lord, what do You want to say to me today?" Then I listen quietly for the Spirit. The more aware we are that God speaks personally, the more important it is to read the Bible regularly and to apply discernment to what we are hearing. Knowing how to confirm God's voice adds greater certainty to my own decision making. Before I learned to distinguish what He was saying, I was sometimes fearful. I'd weigh pros and cons, ask for godly advice, and seek understanding from Scripture—but I didn't always have confidence I was making the right choice. I still take those steps. Now I also expect the Holy Spirit to speak into the process, to confirm or deter, and to give me an inner settledness when I am on the right path. Because He leads me in choices day by day, I know I can count on Him to lead me in big matters too.[7]

What are three steps you can take to carve out time in your life to listen to God's voice?

_____

_____

_____

Help me, almighty God, not to ever be so preoccupied with myself and my little world that I don't take time to be still and know that You are God. In Christ's name, Amen.

Notes

1. Regina Franklin, Who Calls Me Beautiful? (Grand Rapids, MI: Discovery House Publishers, 2004), p. 43.
2. Peter Scazzero, Emotionally Healthy Spirituality (Nashville, TN: Thomas Nelson Publishers, 2006), pp. 53-54.
3. Ibid.
4. Robert Benson, The Echo Within (Colorado Springs, CO: WaterBrook, 2009), pp. 56-57.
5. Mandisa, quoted in Camerin Courtney, "TCW Talks to Mandisa," Today's Chris- tian Woman, July/August 2009, p. 18.
6. Richard A. Swenson, The Overload Syndrome (Colorado Springs, CO: NavPress, 1998), p. 37.
7. Roc Bottomly, "A God Who Speaks," Discipleship Journal, January/February 2009, p. 52.

WEEK EIGHT: LIVE POWERFULLY

SCRIPTURE MEMORY VERSE
His divine power has given us everything we need for life and godliness through our knowledge of him who called us by his own glory and goodness. 2 Peter 1:3

Everything we need.

That, my friend, is what you and I have been given by a gracious and loving God. At least everything we need to live God's purpose for our lives. And to top it off, He also grants us the divine power to make it happen. Of course, we cannot fulfill His purpose in our own strength or in our own wisdom. But as we respond to the One who called us by his own glory and goodness, we can truly live powerfully – inside and out.

In my interactive guidebook *Soul Strong – 7 Keys to a Vibrant Life*, I reflect on what I've personally discovered about the key to living powerfully. "It's not just a matter of physical perseverance or even mental determination. It's a deep commitment and an even deeper empowerment. I call it soul strong."[1]

If we are encouraged by cultural catchphrases such as "You've got what it takes!", then how much more should we believe God when He says we have all we need? Do you ever wonder if you have "what it takes" to live a healthy and balanced life? Well, wonder no more—you do!

What does this week's memory verse say is the source of our provision?

_____
_____
_____

What did God do for us?

_____
_____
_____

Now, keep repeating this phrase as you take a long walk today: "I've got what it takes!"

God's purpose for us is that we receive the divine power He has for us. He wants us to be strong, not weak. In what areas do you feel weak today?

_____

_____

_____

The power and strength of God lives within us by His Holy Spirit, and the revelation of that truth releases spiritual *power in our lives that strengthens both our bodies and spirits. The Greek word dunamis* is often used in reference to the power of the Holy Spirit available to us. This word is the root word of "dynamic," "dynamo" and "dynamite." Dynamite power, by way of the Holy Spirit, enables us to be dynamic witnesses, more than conquerors—spiritual dynamos—and stronger people.

—— DAY 1: PRAY FOR POWER

Holy Spirit, dwell within me and grant me the dynamic power that only You provide. In Christ's name, Amen.

Read Ephesians 3:14-21. Paul knew God's power in a personal way. He experienced it every day of his life, and testified to it when he wrote to the believers at Ephesus. He prayed that they, too, would receive this power. Write down verse 16, and substitute your name for the word "you."

_____

_____

_____

From where does the power come?

_____

_____

_____

And where does he pray you would receive such power?

_____

_____

_____

Paul prays in verses 18 and 19 for power in you so that what things might result?

You may have _____ to grasp how _____
and _____ and _____ and _____
is the _____ of Christ, and to _____ the
_____ that surpasses all knowledge –
that you may be _____ to the measure of all the
_____ of God.

Love seems to be a key concept that God longs for us to understand in order to
experience His full power. What is the hardest part for you of grasping God's unconditional love?

_____
_____
_____

Paul closes his prayer for the Ephesians with a doxology that praises "the God who
is able to do more than all we ask or imagine." Do you sometimes secretly feel your
quest for a healthy weight or emotional healing is too much for God to accomplish?
What would it take for you to believe that God can do even more than what you ask
or imagine?

_____
_____
_____
_____

How does verse 20 say that God accomplishes these things for us?

_____
_____
_____
_____

Have you prayed for God's divine power to fill your life so that you may fulfill God's
purpose for you? Write a simple prayer here, closing with your own doxology of praise:

_____
_____
_____
_____

Heavenly Father, help me remember today that nothing is impossible with You, even on my journey towards balanced health. In Christ's name, Amen.

—— DAY 2: SOURCE OF POWER

Father, please help me when I'm tempted to go back to my old ways and try to accomplish goals through my own strength. In Christ's name, Amen.

Read Galatians 3:1-5. How do we daily tap into the Source of all power? By spending time in the Spirit's presence through daily spiritual disciplines that include prayer, a study of God's Word and meditation. Too often we either skip this aspect of our lives or fast-forward it and thus we move forward only in our own power. While we may be blessed with a certain amount of strength, we inevitably come to the end of our resources all too soon and then find ourselves "running on empty."

First Place for Health offers many resources to guide in proper nutrition through the Live It program. There is a good balance between protein and carbohydrates and good fats. Taken in proper doses, our bodies function more efficiently with the right foods in the right amounts. This is an amazing discovery for any former fast-food junkies used to piling on empty calories only to discover more hunger than satisfaction.

But some of us also suffer from being spiritual fast-food junkies. Our devotional lives have devolved into quickly checking in with God, reading a verse, tossing up a prayer and being on our way. Perhaps you can relate to this woman's struggle:

> I had allowed deadlines, projects, and demands to take priority over my relationship with the Lord. Oh, I still had a quiet time— of sorts. I usually managed to get in some sort of spiritual meal. But all too frequently, that meal had come to consist of hurriedly reading a short passage of scripture just before running out the door to accomplish one more thing for God. Spiritually, I was living in fast-food drive-through's. I was having my devotions, if you could call it that. But I wasn't having devotion. I wasn't meeting with God. I wasn't nurturing our relationship.[2]

How can you move beyond "fast food" devotions to those that nourish your soul? In Paul's letter to the Galatians, he chastises believers for "beginning with the Spirit" but then "trying to attain your goal by human effort."

As you think of your lifelong journey to better health, how would you describe your earlier efforts, before First Place for Health?

_____
_____
_____

What about now? Do you find that you still have a tendency to rely on your willpower alone?

_____
_____
_____

What does Paul call folks who do such things (v. 3)?

_____
_____

What do you do when you want to grow a friendship?

_____
_____
_____

What parallels can you draw with growing your friendship/relationship with God?

_____
_____
_____

Dearest Jesus, spending time with You is important and life-giving. May I always seek You first in my daily schedule. In Christ's name, Amen.

—— DAY 3: EMPOWERED FROM ABOVE
Lord, I do have faith but I'm not always sure how that should be manifested in my life. Show me, please. In Christ's name, Amen.

I may be like some other First Place for Health members, in that my hardest commitment to keep is daily exercise. It seems that both my mind and body often rebel at this activity, which is necessary for balanced living. Am I doomed to failure? No, God has given us everything we need—even to get these bodies moving, no matter what comes our way.

Read John 14:12-19. What are some of the promises Jesus makes in verses 12-14?

_____

_____

_____

Which Person of the Trinity is promised to live within you (vv. 16-17)?

_____

_____

_____

How does the Spirit fulfill in your life Christ's promise in verses 18-19?

_____

_____

_____

Exercising isn't just good for your body; it's good for your soul. One fitness instructor reminds us that it's important to nourish your mind, body and spirit: "The road to wellness is a journey, not a destination. Wake up fifteen minutes earlier and practice deep breathing exercises while you pray. And, remember, working out five to ten minutes a day is one hundred percent better than zero! It's never too late to start."[3]

There are other benefits to being physically fit, including:
- It helps the body burn fat and protects against the muscle loss associated with low-calorie eating plans.
- It helps the body maintain or increase its metabolic rate; may help suppress appetite.
- It allows for weight loss on a higher calorie eating plan, which helps the body get all the nutrients it needs.
- It improves mood and self-esteem.
- It results in important health benefits such as lower blood pressure, improved cholesterol levels and increased fitness.
- It promotes long-term weight maintenance.

Have you asked God to help you exercise each day? If not, do so now in a short prayer.

_____

_____

_____

Thank You, Lord, for getting me moving more each day and for helping me overcome any sedentary tendencies. In Christ's name, Amen.

—— DAY 4: POWER AND PEACE
Holy Spirit, I need You as my Counselor and my Guide. Amen.

Our world has recently lived through more than two years where most of us felt powerless. It was a debilitating and demoralizing feeling. We want to do something, anything, to make something happen, but all too often we just throw our hands up in the air and admit defeat. We feel powerless against all odds. Health is an area where this occurs, often because we feel at the mercy of our own bodies, which seem to rebel against us—even when we're trying to do the right thing for them! That's why we conclude this final week with this important reminder. We are not powerless—we have power from God through the Holy Spirit. We can do what He calls us to do, not in our own strength and will, but in partnership with Him.

Read John 14:25-27. What does Jesus call the Holy Spirit?

_____

_____

_____

What does He say about what the Holy Spirit will do in your life?

_____

_____

_____

Jesus says that He leaves us with peace. When was the last time you experienced peace?

_____

_____

_____

Jesus points out that His peace is nothing like the peace we find in the world. His peace comes in the midst of chaos. It is the sense of wellbeing and full trust that, though the world around you is going crazy, God is still on the throne. He is in control. Be at peace.

The last part of verse 27 gives what admonition?

Do not _____ and do not _____

How could you experience God's peace today? Try withdrawing from your normal habitat (where everything around you calls out for attention) and being still before the Lord. Write down some words you associate with the concept of "peace."

_____

_____

_____

For me it has been helpful to occasionally go for a whole day unplugged away from all my technology. I don't answer my cell phone (unless it's an emergency, of course), don't check my email, don't log into Facebook or do an Instagram update. When I'm deliberately unavailable, God makes His presence known to me in a new way.

If you chose to do this experiment, what did you notice about being "unplugged"?

_____

_____

_____

Author Fil Anderson shares how he came to a point where he had to make some hard choices for turning off the world occasionally so that he could tune in to God:

> With pagers and cell phones, faxes and instant messaging, email and voice mail, streaming audio and video, the world is simply too much with us I could see the striking contrast between my empty life and the promise of a life of peace. I could see that each misfit part of my soul was sewn to the others with one common thread: distractions, keeping me from hearing the true voice of God. I was too distracted and consumed with activity to notice the quiet Voice. My deafness produced a life without peace.[4]

With your planner and your journal, schedule for periodic times away when you can focus on God and your life. Start with an afternoon and perhaps work into one day a month for a quiet retreat. God will meet you there and fill you with His power.

Prince of Peace, will You come into my heart and fill me with a knowledge that You are in control and all is well? In Christ's name, Amen.

—— DAY 5: SPEAK UP

Show me, Father, all the victories You have been working in my life so far. In Christ's name, Amen.

Read 2 Corinthians 4:13-18. The word "therefore" in this Scripture passage is almost like an equal sign (=). Thus viewed, how would you fill in this equation (using verse 13)?

I _____ = I _____

We _____ = We _____

How do you feel about speaking of what God has done in your life?

_____
_____
_____

People can argue with our theology, but they can't dispute our testimony of what actually happened in our lives. That's why sharing true stories is so important. What does verse 15 say the intended outcome is from sharing your testimony?

_____
_____
_____

Are you ever tempted to "lose heart"? List what verse 16 says as:

Reason to lose heart: _____

Reason to take heart: _____

As you look back at these three months of Bible study, list your own:

Reasons to lose heart

_____
_____
_____

Reasons to take heart

_____
_____
_____

Now list your own "light and momentary troubles."

_____

_____

_____

_____

According to verse 17 why are those troubles in your life?

_____

_____

_____

Perhaps you think you are not as far along the path of balanced health as you want to be. But remember: What you see is not all there is to reality! How is that elaborated on in verse 18?

_____

_____

_____

Heavenly Father, truly there are things to share with others, and I'm so grateful that You will help me speak up with good news. In Christ's name, Amen.

—— DAY 6: REFLECTION AND APPLICATION
Lord, You have called me and You will send me and, by Your grace, I will follow where You lead. In Christ's name, Amen.

As we begin to finish this Bible study, I hope you have entered a certain level of familiarity and understanding in your group. How great it would be if the fellowship and sharing could always continue! Perhaps they can, either with this group or in another time and place. But growing and learning together is not all God has purposed for His followers.

Read Jeremiah 1:4-10. He also calls us to go out into the world. How is this concept described in verse 5?

_____

_____

_____

What is your usual response when you feel God is asking you to do a hard thing?

_____

_____

_____

Even though I've been a professional speaker my entire adult life, I still sometimes feel inadequate about speaking of faith matters to others. When Jeremiah protested that he was too young and inexperienced to do what God commanded, what six things did God say in response (vv. 7-9)?

Do not say _____

You must go _____

You must say _____

Do not be _____

I am _____

I will _____

God will also put His words into my mouth! If you wonder how this can happen for you, remember the exercise you worked through on Week 1, Day 4, where you prepared a short testimony of what God has done in your life. Practice sharing it, and then when the time comes, you will be ready!

In verse 10 of Jeremiah 1, God reveals His purpose for Jeremiah's life, which includes an appointment to do six things:

1. _____

2. _____

3. _____

4. _____

5. _____

6. _____

Is there one of these that might apply to your life's purpose, too? Explain.

_____

_____

_____

Thanks, God, for the story You have woven throughout my life. Please help me share it often, with humility and purpose. In Christ's name, Amen.

—— DAY 7: REFLECTION AND APPLICATION

Help me, precious Lord, to keep going even when I feel disillusioned or discouraged, knowing that You are not finished with me yet. Amen.

We may be near the end of studying *God's Purpose for You*, but we are always on the journey of discovering more of what God has for us. Now that we have looked at all God has done and all we have done, the question is, Can we keep on going—step by step—living a balanced life in God's will and God's way? The answer can be a re-sounding yes! By the grace of God, we can!

In Philippians 1:6, Paul states that the source of his confidence is that "He who be-gan a good work in [us] will carry it on to completion until the day of Christ Jesus." Our part in the walk of faith is to keep walking. Look up the definition of "persever-ance" and write it here:

_____

_____

_____

Are you ever worried that you won't be able to continue the commitments and growth you have experienced spiritually, physically, mentally and emotionally when your time in *God's Purpose for You* is over? If so, what do you believe is the source of that concern?

_____

_____

_____

Isaiah 50:7 reminds us that the Sovereign Lord helps us: "I will not be _____!" However, he says he must do something (v. 7b). What is that?

_____

_____

_____

What would doing that look like in your life ahead?

_____

_____

_____

Thank You, Lord, for continuing to guide me on a path of purpose, peace, and power in every area of my life. With Your help, I know I can live soul strong.! In Christ's name, Amen.

I would like to close this study by offering a blessing over you, based on God's Word.

O people, the LORD has told you what is good,
and this is what he requires of you:
to do what is right, to love mercy,
and to walk humbly with your God.
Micah 6.8 NLT

A Blessing for Purpose

I know you want to live a whole and healthy life,
full of purpose, full of service, full of significance.
May you always remember how much God loves you.
His plans for you are good and they include your doing good.
May you daily choose what is right,
that your body and soul may thrive.
May you daily love mercy,
serving others with compassion and courage.
May you walk forward into each new day,
grasping tightly to the Lover of your soul.
And in every ordinary and extraordinary moment,
may you glorify God and enjoy Him forever.
Choose wisely.
Your life matters.

~ *Lucinda Secrest McDowell*

Notes

1. Lucinda Secrest McDowell, Soul Strong – 7 Keys to a Vibrant Life (Birmingham AL: New Hope Publishers, 2020), p. xiv.
2. Nancy Leigh DeMoss, A Place of Quiet Rest (Chicago, IL: Moody Publishers, 2000).
3. Theresa Rowe, "Soul Trainer," Guideposts, February 2009, p. 79.
4. Fil Anderson, Running on Empty (Colorado Springs, CO: NavPress, 2004) pp. 13,23.

WEEK NINE: A TIME TO CELEBRATE

During this study we have examined many ways that God provides refuge. We've learned about false refuges, why we might flee to them, and how we can exchange them for God's true refuge. Our goal has been to strengthen our dependence on Him and know Him more. This week you will reflect on how God has spoken to you during this session. To help you shape your short victory celebration testimony, work through the following questions in your prayer journal, one on each day leading up to your group's celebration.

DAY ONE: List some of the benefits you have gained by allowing the Lord to transform your life through this twelve-week First Place for Health session. Be mindful that He has been active in all four aspects of your being, so list benefits you have received in the physical, mental, emotional and spiritual realms.

DAY TWO: In what ways have you most significantly changed mentally? Have you seen a shift in the ways you think about yourself, food, your relationships, or God? How has Scripture memory been a part of these shifts?

DAY THREE: In what ways have you most significantly changed emotionally? Have you begun to identify how your feelings influence your relationship to food and exercise? What are you doing to stay aware of your emotions, both positive and negative?

DAY FOUR: In what ways have you most significantly changed spiritually? How has your relationship with God deepened? How has drawing closer to Him made a difference in the other three areas of your life?

DAY FIVE: In what ways have you most significantly changed physically? Have you met or exceeded your weight/measurement goals? How has your health improved during the past twelve weeks?

DAY SIX: Was there one person in your First Place for Health group who was particularly encouraging to you? How did their kindness make a difference in your First Place for Health journey?

DAY SEVEN: Summarize the previous six questions into a one-page testimony, or "faith story," to share at your group's victory celebration.

May our Mighty God make you victorious in Him, as you continue to keep Him first in all things!

LEADER DISCUSSION GUIDE

For in-depth information, guidance and helpful tips about leading a successful First Place for Health group, spend time studying the *My Place for Leadership* book. In it, you will find valuable answers to most of your questions, as well as personal insights from many First Place for Health group leaders.

For the group meetings in this session, be sure to read and consider each week's discussion topics several days before the meeting—some questions and activities require supplies and/or planning to complete. Also, if you are leading a large group, plan to break into smaller groups for discussion and then come together as a large group to share your answers and responses. Make sure to appoint a capable leader for each small group so that discussions stay focused and on track (and be sure each group records their answers!).

—— WEEK ONE: DISCOVER PURPOSE

Go over each of the four health areas—physical, mental, spiritual, and emotional—and have members share what they believe God's way is for us in each of those areas. (It's especially good if they have a Scripture to back up what they are saying.)

As we begin our nine-week study of *God's Purpose for You*, write down what you think your purpose is, and put today's date next to your words. It will be interesting to see if that changes over the course of these next weeks.

On Day 1 we looked at the life of Caleb. What did you learn from him about how body and soul health work in tandem?

Was Day 3 a wake up call for you? How are you living intentionally today?

Which of the 5 purposes listed in Day 5 do you find the most challenging, and why?

On Day 7 you were invited to respond wholeheartedly to seeking God's purposes. What is your honest response?

Recite together this week's memory verse and discuss why First Place for Health emphasizes Scripture memory.

—— WEEK TWO: DESIRE CHANGE

Ask participants to discuss some of the hardest times of change they have encountered in their lives so far and how they handled those changes. Did it make a difference if it was change they chose or change that just happened to them?

Ask members if they found it uncomfortable or awkward to identify their deepest desires. Was it hard to write them down? Why?

Have someone read the story of the man at the pool of Bethesda in John 5:1-9. What are some of the group's reactions to that story?

Does anyone believe that Jesus is asking him or her, "Do you want to get well?" If so, what is that person's answer?

Ask for a volunteer to explain the metamorphosis of a caterpillar to a butterfly. Then point out that change of that kind is what we called "transformation." A caterpillar doesn't become a faster caterpillar, but a totally new creature—one that can soar. Paul uses this same root word (*metamorphoo*) to describe what God wants to do in transforming us— changing from the inside out. Ask the group to dream about the totally new creature they could become with this kind of transformation. Have them draw a picture that gives hints of that result. (Note: the drawing doesn't have to be of their new body; it could be a pair of running shoes or a new hairdo or a symbol of a trip or anything that might reflect the goal they hope to achieve.)

Ask participants if they have appropriated the Holy Spirit's power that is available for every follower of Christ. Have them try to identify the difference that might occur in various areas of their lives by comparing "in our own power" versus "through God's power of the Holy Spirit."

Discuss where they have gone to seek life rather than to God. Do they have something else to replace that now that they've been learning about living a balanced life? Ask for examples.

Ask members to pair up as partners (or use their prayer partners if they already have paired up for that) and have each person identify one change he or she hopes to see by the end of this 9-week session. Ask the pairs to commit to praying daily about that change in their partner.

Close with a reading of Jeremiah 29:11 and a prayer.

—— WEEK THREE: LOVE GOD

Share ways each of us can love God by going daily into each of the "four rooms of our house" (see Day 2)—body, soul, mind and spirit.

On Day 3, members read that we love God by keeping His commands.

Discuss what are we saying to God when we don't keep His commands. Which of God's commands are especially hard for the members to keep?

Ask if anyone cares to share briefly (no names, please) his or her own experience with a "frenemy." What can such encounters teach us about how our actions speak volumes regarding our love for God?

Ask each member to share one thing God has done for him or her out of His great love. Next, ask the group as a whole when the last time they shared with someone else how God has loved them. Challenge them to seek an opportunity to do so this week.

Read 1 John 4:17-21 and ask who might want to share some of the fears they wrote about on Day 6.

Discuss why is it important that those who love God also love others.

Have a volunteer read the definitions of "omniscient," "omnipotent" and "omnipresent" from Day 7. Ask the group to share which of these attributes they most appreciate or need from God this week.

End your session by asking everyone to close his or her eyes while one person reads aloud the love letter from God on Day 7.

—— WEEK FOUR: STAND STRONG

Go around the group and ask the group to share aloud one of the strongholds they identified on Day 1. Mention that they are allowed to say "pass" if they prefer not to share.

Have a volunteer read Ephesians 6:10-18, and then go over the table everyone completed on Day 1, emphasizing what spiritual armor does for us.

Ask for volunteers to share how they felt on Day 2 about identifying Satan as an enemy, villain and foe.

Review the five ways God comes to us in strength (see the list on Day 3). Have participants discuss which particular ones speak to them, and why.

Ask for a volunteer to share why King David talked so much about God protecting and rescuing him. Refer to lists on Day 4 and point out ways that God did this. Next, go over your own lists from Day 4 and share similarly what God is doing to keep you strong.

On Day 6, members were asked if there is anything they need to lay aside in order to pursue their relationship with God. What did some of the members identify?

Soldiers of the Roman Empire became lazy and undisciplined, until eventually they were unable to sustain victorious strength (see Day 7). Ask members what they are doing daily to prepare so that they will prevail as battles arise

—— WEEK FIVE: SEARCH INWARD

Ask if anyone is willing to share how he or she turned to food (or any other substance/habit) to meet needs that only God can meet.

On Day 1, we were encouraged to ask God to bring into the light some things about us we had pushed deep into dark corners of our lives. Ask if anyone would be willing to share this process.

Have a volunteer read Ephesians 2:1-10, and ask the members which verse in that section spoke loudest to them, and why.

Ask members it they agree with the statement that if we truly embraced the meaning of Ephesians 2:8-9, our lives would be changed forever. Why or why not? What do they now believe about God's grace in their lives?

Discuss some of the consequences those in the group experienced be- fore begin- ning their journey to balanced health.

Ask if anyone in the group can relate to Mandisa's story on Day 3 of how she responded when she was humiliated on American Idol. What was the "takeaway" for them?

It's a great blessing that we can go directly to God at all times in all places. As you review Day 5, share some ways with the group that they can make "spiritual deposits" in God's presence.

Ask members to share how definitions of beauty influenced them while growing up, for better or for worse.

Ask participants to think of someone whose inner beauty attracts him or her to them (see Day 6). What are those characteristics displayed, and how can each of us get them, too?

On Day 7 participants were asked to "become like Christ by practicing the types of activities He engaged in." Can they think of an instance in which they have done this?

—— WEEK SIX: OVERCOME CHALLENGES

How do the members identify with Paul's struggles of doing what he does not want to do and not doing what he knows he should do (see Day 1)?

Ask participants to describe the last time their own version of "Flesh Woman" or "Flesh Man" showed up and took over. What were the results?

Have the group share the particulars about a time when someone comforted them. What did they learn that will help them comfort someone else in the future?

Ask for volunteers in your group who either were adopted or have adopted a child to share their experience briefly. What do you think God wants to communicate to us through the adoption analogy we studied on Day 3?

Paul listed many of the obstacles that were powerful but still helpless to put a wedge between him and God (see Day 4). Ask members what encouragement this gives them. What obstacles are they up against on their journey to balanced health?

On Day 5, prayer is mentioned as a powerful weapon for those hoping to overcome the world. An example of prayer is given. Ask members to share other helpful prayers or places where they find prayers to sustain them.

Go around the circle and ask each person to share how he or she is "new" since beginning this study.

Have someone read Psalm 73:21-28 and then discuss phrases that members of the group might feel expresses where they are or have been.

Close in prayer, suggesting that each person surrender to God any part of his or her life that he or she has been holding back and asking God to fill each person. Use the prayer from Day 7, "God, this day is for You."

—— WEEK SEVEN: RESPOND FAITHFULLY

Have group members share about the pros and cons of having a GPS system or using Google Maps and how that relates to responding to God's voice.

Day 1 presents a sort of bad news/good news story of God and the Israelites. Ask members how they would describe it and what important points they are to take to heart from it.

Have members share a time when God shouted at them through a "megaphone of pain" (Day 2), and their eventual response.

Ask the group what negative messages from their past are still replayed occasionally in their minds. When they choose to believe those messages, what happens?

On Day 3, participants were asked to check off three positive statements they wanted to embrace this week. Go around and have each person share one each.

Have a volunteer read the quote about overload from Dr. Richard Swenson (see Day 7), and then ask people to share their current struggles and victories in this area.

Ask for volunteers to share the results of their time in solitude and silence (see Day 7) and how it impacted them. Take time to have everyone in the group jot down a note, planning a time for solitude and silence in the week ahead

—— WEEK EIGHT: LIVE POWERFULLY

Often we complain about how hard it is to lead a godly life, yet our memory verse this week says we have everything we need to do just that. Discuss some of the reasons why we still struggle.

Share from your notes on Days 1 and 2 how you can use the Spirit's power in your own life. Name some instances when relying on willpower alone caused you to fail at balanced healthy living.

Ask volunteers to give examples from Day 3 of choices they made directed by their sinful nature. Contrast those choices with choices they could have made instead—choices directed by the Spirit.

Discuss why the Holy Spirit's identity as "Counselor" is appealing or not.

Have a group discussion concerning their various struggles and accomplishments in the exercise arena during first seven weeks.

When we are overstressed and agitated, we need to remind ourselves to breathe. Discuss why stopping to take a long breath is a step toward calm and serenity.

Go around the group and share specific distractions you each have. Then have someone read aloud the quote by Fil Anderson on Day 4.

Challenge each person to write down a time this coming week when they will seek God through solitude and silence.

Ask how people feel about the concept in Jeremiah 1 (see Day 6) of being sent by God to speak to others of spiritual things.

Ask participants if they have both *confidence* and *perseverance*, and how they know.

Go around the group and have each person pinpoint one thing they now believe is God's purpose for them. Close in a prayer of thanksgiving and commitment.

—— WEEK NINE: TIME TO CELEBRATE

As your class members reflect on each week's content, help them remember the ways strength has risen because of following Christ fully in each area of life. Ask: What have you learned in this study that has made you stronger?

FIRST PLACE FOR HEALTH
JUMP START MENUS

All recipe and menu nutritional information was determined using the Master-Cook software, a program that accesses a database containing more than 6,000 food items prepared using the United States Department of Agriculture (USDA) publications and information from food manufacturers. As with any nutritional program, MasterCook calculates the nutritional values of the recipes based on ingredients. Nutrition may vary due to how the food is prepared, where the food comes from, soil content, season, ripeness, processing and method of preparation. For these reasons, please use the recipes and menu plans as approximate guides. As always, consult your physician and/or a registered dietitian before starting a weight-loss program.

For those who need more calories,

add the following to the 1,400–1,500 calorie plan:

1,500-1,600 calories:	1 oz.-eq of protein, 1 oz.-eq. grains, ½ cup vegetables, 1 tsp. healthy oils
1,700-1,800 calories:	1½ oz.-eq. of protein, 2 oz.-eq. grains, 1 cup of vegetables, 1 tsp. healthy oils
1,900-2,000 calories:	2 oz.-eq. of protein, 2 oz.-eq. of grains, 1 cup vegetables, ½ cup fruit, 1 tsp. healthy oils
2,100-2,200 calories:	3 oz.-eq. of protein, 3 oz.-eq. grains, 1½ cup vegetables, ½ cup fruit, 2 tsp. healthy oils
2,300-2,400 calories:	4 oz.-eq. of protein, 4 oz.-eq. of grains, 2 cups vegetables 3 cups frit, 3 tsp. healthy oils

Apple Flapjacks

3/4 cup sifted flour
1/2 tsp. baking powder
1/4 tsp. cinnamon
1 1/2 tsp. vegetable oil
1 1/2 tsp. sugar
1/4 cup egg substitute
1 cup apple, finely chopped
1/2 cup skim milk
Nonstick cooking spray

Sift flour with baking powder and cinnamon. Mix oil, sugar, egg substitute and apple. Combine wet and dry ingredients, gradually adding in milk. Spray a nonstick griddle with vegetable spray. Bake flapjacks on griddle as for pancakes. Sprinkle with brown sugar substitute if desired. Serves 4.

Nutritional Information: 202 calories; 5g fat (22.2% calories from fat); 7g protein; 33g carbohydrate; 2g dietary fiber; 1mg cholesterol; 143mg sodium.

Chicken and Spinach Salad

    2 cups cooked chicken, cubed
    6 cups packed fresh spinach torn into bite-sized pieces
    2 oranges, peeled and cut into chunks
    2 cups fresh strawberries, sliced

In large bowl, combine chicken, spinach, oranges and strawberries. Toss with chilled Orange-Poppy Dressing (see following recipe) just before serving. Serves 4. Serve each with 6 slices melba toast.

Nutritional Information (1 1/4 cups): 200 calories; 5.8 g total fat; 4 mg cholesterol; 355 mg sodium; 29 g carbohydrates; 5.9 g fiber; 8.6 g protein;

Orange Poppy Seed Dressing

    2 tbsp. red wine vinegar
    3 tbsp. orange juice
    1 1/2 tbsp. canola oil
    1/4 tsp. dry mustard
    1/4 tsp. poppy seeds

Nutritional Information: 257 Calories; 9g Fat (31.2% calories from fat); 25g Protein; 20g Carbohydrate; 5g Dietary Fiber; 60mg Cholesterol; 128mg Sodium.

Scallops with Soba Noodles with Steamed Peas Vinaigrette

3 tablespoons low-sodium soy sauce

1 tablespoon fresh orange juice

1 tablespoon rice vinegar

1 tablespoon honey

1/2 teaspoon bottled ground fresh ginger

1/4 teaspoon chili garlic sauce

1 tablespoon dark sesame oil, divided

1 pound large sea scallops

4 cups hot cooked soba (about 6 ounces uncooked buckwheat noodles)

1/8 teaspoon salt

1/4 cup thinly sliced green onions

Combine first 6 ingredients and 1 teaspoon oil in a shallow baking dish; add scallops to dish in a single layer. Marinate 4 minutes on each side. Heat remaining 2 teaspoons oil in a large skillet over medium-high heat. Remove scallops from dish, reserving marinade. Add scallops to pan; sauté 1 minute on each side or until almost done. Remove scallops from pan; keep warm. Place remaining marinade in pan; bring to a boil. Return scallops to pan; cook 1 minute. Toss noodles with salt and green onions. Place 1 cup noodle mixture on each of 4 plates. Top each serving with about 3 scallops, and drizzle with 1 tablespoon sauce. Serve with Steamed Peas Vinaigrette Serves 4

Steamed Peas Vinaigrette

Steam 1 cup snow peas and 1 cup trimmed sugar snap peas, covered, 3 minutes or until crisp-tender. Combine with 1/3 cup thinly sliced radishes. Combine 1 tablespoon rice vinegar, 1 tablespoon soy sauce, 2 teaspoons canola oil, 1 1/2 teaspoons mirin, 1/4 teaspoon black pepper, and 1/8 teaspoon kosher salt; stir with a whisk. Pour over peas mixture; toss.

Nutritional Information: 315 calories; 4.5g fat (13% calories from fat); 28g protein; 42.7g carbohydrate; 1.9g dietary Fiber; 37mg cholesterol; 653mg sodium.

Cran-Apple Oatmeal

2 cups skim milk
1/3 cup dried cranberries
1/2 tsp. ground cinnamon
1/4 tsp. salt
1 cup oats, rolled (raw) and uncooked
1 chopped apple
2 packets Sweet 'n Low® sweetener or 1 tsp. sugar
1/2 tsp. vanilla

Combine milk, cranberries, cinnamon and salt in a medium saucepan. Bring to a boil over medium heat, stirring occasionally. Add oats and apple. Simmer uncovered for 5 to 6 minutes for old-fashioned oats or 1 to 2 minutes for quick oats, stirring occasionally until most of liquid has been absorbed. Remove from heat. Stir in sweetener/sugar and vanilla. Serves 2.

Nutritional Information: 287 calories; 3g fat (10% calories from fat); 15g protein; 50g carbohydrate; 6g dietary Fiber; 4mg cholesterol; 398mg sodium

Grilled Chicken and Pineapple Sandwiches

4 (6-ounce) skinless, boneless chicken breast halves
1/2 teaspoon salt
1/4 teaspoon freshly ground black pepper
Cooking spray
1/4 cup fresh lime juice (about 2 limes)
4 (1/2-inch-thick) slices fresh pineapple
4 (1.5-ounce) whole wheat hamburger buns, toasted
Light mayonnaise (optional)
4 large basil leaves

Prepare grill. Sprinkle chicken evenly with salt and pepper. Place chicken on grill rack coated with cooking spray; grill 5 to 6 minutes on each side or until done, brushing occasionally with lime juice. Grill pineapple 2 to 3 minutes on each side or until browned. Spread mayonnaise on bottom halves of buns, if desired. Top each with 1 chicken breast half, 1 pineapple slice, 1 basil leaf, and 1 bun top. Serves 4. Serve with 1 oz. baked chips.

Nutritional Information: 444 calories; 5g fat (12.8% calories from fat); 47.4g protein; 52.5g carbohydrate; 6.1g dietary fiber; 99mg cholesterol; 770mg sodium.

Steak Salad Wraps

1 ½ lb. seasoned beef for fajitas
½ cup blue cheese dressing
2 tomatoes, chopped
1 small red onion, thinly sliced
1 bag baby spring mix
8 spinach or sun-dried tomato tortilla wraps
nonstick cooking spray

On the grill: Spray the grill rack with nonstick cooking spray. Prepare charcoal or gas grill for cooking. Place fajitas on the grill rack. Cook each side for 8 to 10 minutes or until fully cooked. Cut meat across the grain into ½-inch strips.

In the skillet: Cut meat across the grain into ½-inch strips. Heat skillet for three minutes over high heat. Spray a pan with nonstick cooking. Cook beef, stirring every 2 to 3 minutes until meat is fully cooked. Place cooked fajita meat on one end of large serving platter. Arrange blue cheese dressing, tomatoes, onion, spring mix, and spinach or sun-dried-tomato tortilla wraps on the other end of the platter. Let everyone combine his or her own wrap. Serve with 1 cup Mixed Fruit Salad. Serves 8.

Mixed Fruit Salad
2 bananas, sliced
2 apples, diced
(2) 8-oz. cans of pineapple chunks with juice
2 cups grapes

Combine all and serve.

Nutritional Information: 475 calories; 19g fat (35.8% calories from fat); 19g protein; 57g carbohydrate; 7g dietary fiber; 52mg cholesterol; 568mg sodium.

Tip: pineapple juice keeps fruit salad fresh for three days.

Carole's Breakfast Surprise

1 6 oz. carton Yoplait Light Orange Crème Yogurt
¼ cup cottage cheese
4 oz. can mandarin oranges (drained)
1 Tbsp. Light Cool Whip

Mix all ingredients and enjoy.

Nutritional Information: 185 Calories; 1g Fat (6.6% calories from fat); 16g Protein; 27g Carbohydrate; 2g Dietary Fiber; 7mg Cholesterol; 337mg Sodium.

Pear-Walnut Sandwiches

1/2 cup (4 ounces) tub-style light cream cheese
8 (1.1-ounce) slices cinnamon-raisin bread, toasted
2 tablespoons finely chopped walnuts, toasted
2 Bartlett pears, cored and thinly sliced
1 cup alfalfa sprouts

Spread 1 tablespoon cream cheese evenly over each of 8 bread slices. Sprinkle 1/2 tablespoon walnuts evenly over each of 4 bread slices. Top each evenly with pear slices, sprouts, and 1 bread slice. Cut each sandwich in half diagonally. Serves 4. Serve with 1 cup nonfat milk.

Nutritional Information: 421 calories; 11g fat (22.8% calories from fat); 16.7g protein; 64.2g carbohydrate; 5.2g dietary fiber; 19mg cholesterol; 489mg sodium.

Cajun Spiced Tilapia

1 1/4 lbs. (4 fillets) tilapia
3 tbsp. Tony Cachere Original Creole Seasoning
nonstick cooking spray

Spice tilapia liberally with Creole Seasoning. Heat skillet to medium-high heat and spray with nonstick cooking spray. Add spiced tilapia fillets and grill for 4 minutes on each side. Serve with 2 cups spring mixed with light ranch dressing, 1 cup mashed potatoes and 1 dinner roll. Serves 4.

Nutritional Information: 375 calories; 8g fat (18.7% calories from fat); 33g protein; 43g carbohydrate; 6g dietary fiber; 66mg cholesterol; 725mg sodium.

Egg and Cheese Breakfast Tacos with Homemade Salsa

1 cup chopped tomato
1/4 cup chopped red onion
2 tablespoons chopped fresh cilantro
1 teaspoon minced jalapeño pepper
1/4 teaspoon kosher salt
4 teaspoons fresh lime juice, divided
1 teaspoon minced garlic, divided
1 cup organic refried beans
1/4 teaspoon ground cumin
1 tablespoon 1% low-fat milk
6 large eggs, lightly beaten
Cooking spray
1/4 cup chopped green onions
8 (6-inch) corn tortillas
1/2 cup (2 ounces) shredded Monterey Jack cheese with jalapeño peppers
8 teaspoons reduced-fat sour cream

Combine first 5 ingredients in a small bowl. Stir in 2 teaspoons juice and 1/2 teaspoon garlic. Combine beans, remaining 2 teaspoons juice, remaining 1/2 teaspoon garlic, and cumin in another bowl. Combine milk and eggs in a medium bowl; stir with a whisk. Heat a large nonstick skillet over medium-high heat. Coat pan with cooking spray. Add green onions to pan; sauté 1 minute, stirring frequently. Stir in egg mixture; cook 3 minutes or until soft-scrambled, stirring constantly. Remove from heat. Warm tortillas according to package directions. Spread 1 tablespoon bean mixture on each tortilla. Spoon about 2 tablespoons egg mixture down center of each tortilla. Top each serving with 1 tablespoon tomato mixture, 1 tablespoon cheese, and 1 teaspoon sour cream. Serves 4. Serve with 1 cup of fresh mango.

Nutritional Information: 441 calories; 13.3g fat (26% calories from fat); 20g protein; 62g carbohydrate; 10.5g dietary fiber; 289mg cholesterol; 407mg sodium.

French-style Grilled Ham & Cheese

4 (1 1/2-ounce) slices French bread
4 teaspoons honey mustard
6 ounces reduced-fat deli ham, thinly sliced
4 (1-ounce) slices reduced-fat Swiss cheese
1/2 cup fat-free milk
3 large egg whites
Cooking spray

Cut a slit in each bread slice to form a pocket. Spread 1 teaspoon honey mustard into each bread pocket. Divide ham and cheese evenly among bread pockets. Combine milk and egg whites in a shallow bowl, stirring with a whisk. Dip sandwiches, 1 at a time, in milk mixture, turning to coat. Heat a large nonstick skillet coated with cooking spray over medium-high heat. Add 2 sandwiches; cook 3 minutes on each side or until golden brown. Repeat procedure with remaining sandwiches. Serves 4. Serve with 1 cup berries with 2 tablespoons Cool Whip Lite and 1 ounce pretzel twists.

Nutritional Information: 461 calories; 10.8g fat (22% calories from fat); 22.3g protein; 62g carbohydrate; 5.38g dietary fiber; 40mg cholesterol; 1082mg sodium.

Chili Soup

1 1/2 pounds lean ground beef
1 medium onion, chopped
3 cans minestrone soup, condensed (10-3/4 oz.)
1 can tomatoes, stewed (14-1/2 oz.) diced
1 can tomatoes with green chilies (10 oz.) diced
1 can beans (15-1/2 oz.) chili
4 cups water

Brown together ground beef and chopped onion. Drain thoroughly. Add remaining ingredients and mix together. Simmer for 10 minutes. Serve with 2 cups spring mix salad with light ranch dressing and 1 2-inch cube of cornbread. Serves 12.

Nutritional Information: 438 calories; 18g fat (36.9% calories from fat); 21g protein; 48g carbohydrate; 5g dietary fiber; 69mg cholesterol; 1,018mg sodium.

DAY 5 | BREAKFAST

Veggie Piglets in Blankets with Dipping Sauce

1 (8-ounce) package reduced-fat crescent roll dough
16 meatless breakfast links (such as Boca)
3/4 cup honey
1/4 cup Dijon mustard

Preheat oven to 375°. Unroll dough; divide along perforations into triangles. Cut each dough triangle in half to form 2 triangles. Wrap one dough triangle around center of each breakfast link, starting at wide end of triangle. Arrange wrapped breakfast links on a baking sheet. Bake at 375° for 15 minutes or until browned. Combine honey and mustard; serve with piglets. Serves 8.

Tip – Great for parties and a kid favorite.

Nutritional Information: 227 Calories; 8.2g Fat (30.6% calories from fat); trace Protein; 44.2g Carbohydrate; 2.2g Dietary Fiber; 0mg Cholesterol; 754mg Sodium.

Grilled Ham, Muenster, and Spinach Sandwiches

8 (3/4-ounce) slices crusty Chicago-style Italian bread (about 1/2 inch thick), toasted
8 ounces thinly sliced lower-sodium deli ham
4 (1-ounce) slices reduced-sodium Muenster cheese
1/4 cup Chow Chow
2 cups fresh baby spinach
Cooking spray

Layer each of 4 bread slices with 2 ounces ham, 1 slice Muenster cheese, 1/2 cup baby spinach, 1 tablespoon chowchow, and 1 bread slice. Heat a large nonstick skillet over medium-high heat. Coat sandwiches with cooking spray; add to pan. Cook 2 minutes on each side or until browned and cheese melts. Cut sandwiches in half, if desired. Serve immediately.

Note: Chow Chow is a spicy sweet relish made from cucumbers, onions, peppers and other vegetables. Sweet pickle relish may be substituted if Chow Chow is not available in your area.

Nutritional Information: 315 Calories; 11g Fat (33% calories from fat); 20.8g Protein; 32.4g Carbohydrate; 1.7g Dietary Fiber; 53mg Cholesterol; 821mg Sodium.

Butternut Squash Pizzas

1 cup thinly sliced onion
1/2 butternut squash, seeded and thinly sliced
1 tsp. chopped fresh rosemary
salt and pepper to taste
1 tbsp. olive oil, divided
1 pkg. refrigerated pizza crust
1 tbsp. cornmeal
2 tbsp. grated Parmesan cheese

Preheat oven to 400° F. Place sliced onion and squash in a roasting pan. Sprinkle with rosemary, salt, pepper and 1 tablespoon of the olive oil; toss to coat. Bake in the preheated oven for 20 minutes, or until onions are lightly browned and squash is tender; set aside. Increase oven temperature to 450° F. On a floured surface, roll each ball of dough into an 8-inch round. Place the rounds on a baking sheet sprinkled with cornmeal (you may need 2 baking sheets depending on their size). Distribute squash mixture over the two rounds and continue baking for 10 minutes, checking occasionally, or until the crust is firm. Sprinkle with cheese and the remaining table-spoon olive oil. Cut into quarters, and serve.

Nutritional Information: 342 Calories; 7g Fat (17.6% calories from fat); 10g Protein; 63g Carbohydrate; 4g Dietary Fiber; 2mg Cholesterol; 528mg Sodium.

Raisin French Toast

1 1/2 slices cinnamon-raisin bread
1/2 cup egg substitute
1/4 tsp. vanilla flavoring
1 tbsp. nonfat milk
nonstick cooking spray

In a shallow bowl, combine egg substitute, vanilla and milk. Add slices of bread, turning until egg mixture is absorbed. Spray a small nonstick skillet or griddle with nonstick cooking spray and preheat. Cook the bread over medium heat for 3 to 5 minutes, turning once, until golden brown on both sides. Serve with 1 tablespoon low-sugar syrup, ½ grapefruit sections and 1/2 cup nonfat milk. Serves 1.

Nutritional Information: 431 calories; 14g fat (30.6% calories from fat); 23g protein; 50g carbohydrate; 3g dietary fiber; 5mg cholesterol; 460mg sodium.

Honey-Gingered Carrot Soup & Smoked Turkey Sandwich

3 cups fat-free, less-sodium chicken broth
2 (10-ounce) packages frozen sliced honey-glazed carrots (such as Green Giant), thawed
1/2 cup frozen chopped onion
1 tablespoon minced peeled fresh ginger
1 teaspoon grated orange rind
1/4 teaspoon black pepper
Plain fat-free yogurt (optional)
Thyme sprigs (optional)

Combine first 6 ingredients in a large saucepan; bring to a boil. Reduce heat; simmer 2 minutes or until carrots are tender. Place half of soup mixture in a blender or food processor. Remove center piece of blender lid (to allow steam to escape); secure blender lid on blender. Place a clean towel over opening in blender lid (to avoid splatters). Blend 30 seconds or until smooth. Pour pureed mixture into a large bowl. Repeat procedure with remaining soup mixture. Ladle soup into bowls; garnish with yogurt and thyme sprigs, if desired. Serves 4.

Smoked Turkey Sandwich

2 slices whole wheat bread
2 ounces sliced smoked turkey
1 tablespoon light mayonnaise
2 slices tomato
1 romaine lettuce leaf

Assemble and enjoy with Honey-Gingered Carrot Soup.

Nutritional Information: 394 Calories; 9g Fat (25% calories from fat); 19.7g Protein; 53.7g Carbohydrate; 7.8g Dietary Fiber; 31mg Cholesterol; 1211mg Sodium.

Honey and Spice-Glazed Pork Chops

1/4 cup honey
2 tablespoons Dijon mustard
1/2 teaspoon ground ginger
1/4 teaspoon ground cinnamon
1/8 teaspoon ground cloves
Cooking spray
4 (4-ounce) boneless center-cut loin pork chops (about 1/2 inch thick)
1/2 teaspoon salt
1/4 teaspoon freshly ground black pepper

Combine first 5 ingredients in a bowl. Heat a large nonstick skillet coated with cooking spray over medium-high heat. Sprinkle pork with salt and pepper; cook 2 minutes on each side or until browned. Reduce heat to medium-low; add honey mixture. Cook 10 minutes or until done, turning pork once. Serves 4. Serve with 1/2 cup mashed potatoes and 1 cup steamed green beans.

Nutritional Information: 438 Calories; 14.1g Fat (29% calories from fat); 38g protein; 40.7g Carbohydrate; 6.3g Dietary Fiber; 94mg Cholesterol; 869mg Sodium.

Apple Cinnamon Oatmeal

3 apples (about 3 cups), diced
2 tablespoons water
1 tablespoon butter
1 tablespoon maple syrup
½ teaspoon ground cinnamon
A pinch of sea salt
A drop of pure vanilla extract
2 cups prepared oatmeal

Put diced apple into a large skillet with 2 tablespoons water. Cover the skillet and cook over medium heat for about 5 minutes, stirring occasionally, until the apples become slightly soft.

Add 1 tablespoon butter to skillet. Stir apples and butter together until the apples are well coated. Cook for 5 minutes, stirring, occasionally, until the apples become soft.

Add Maple syrup, cinnamon, salt, and vanilla to the apples, and stir until well mixed. Cook for 5 minutes more, stirring constantly.

In the meantime, prepare oatmeal. Divide into separate bowls and top with caramelized apples, a good drizzle of the cooking juices, and a sprinkle of cinnamon. Serve immediately. Serves 4

Nutritional Information: 236 Calories; 11g Fat; 7g Protein; 31g Carbohydrate; 2g Fiber

Spicy Bistro Steak Subs

1 tablespoon stick margarine
2 garlic cloves, minced
1 pound thinly sliced lean deli roast beef
2 tablespoons ketchup
4 teaspoons Worcestershire sauce
1/2 teaspoon dried basil
1/2 teaspoon dried oregano
1/4 teaspoon ground red pepper
1 1/2 cups beef broth
6 (2 1/2-ounce) hoagie rolls with sesame seeds, cut in half lengthwise
Carrot curls and olives (optional)

Melt margarine in a large nonstick skillet over medium-high heat. Add minced garlic, and sauté 2 minutes. Add roast beef and next 6 ingredients (roast beef through broth), and bring to a boil. Reduce heat, and simmer 2 minutes, stirring frequently. Drain roast beef in a colander over a bowl, reserving sauce. Divide roast beef evenly among roll bottoms, and top with roll tops. Serve sandwiches with reserved sauce. Garnish sandwiches with carrot curls and olives, if desired. Serves 6. Serve with 1 apple.

Nutritional Information: 426 Calories; 10.6g Fat (4.9% calories from fat); 21.4g Protein; 61.6g Carbohydrate; 5.6g Dietary Fiber; 2mg Cholesterol; 938Sodium.

Savory Lamb Chops

2 tablespoons Dijon mustard
2 tablespoons fresh rosemary
or 2 teaspoons dried rosemary, crushed
2 teaspoons honey
1/2 teaspoon coarsely ground pepper
16 ounces lamb chop, lean (4-ounce)

Preheat grill to medium high heat. Combine first 4 ingredients in a small bowl, and stir well. Trim fat from lamb, and place chops on the grill. Grill 5 minutes on each side. Brush mustard mixture over chops. Broil chops 2 minutes on each side or until desired degree of doneness, basting occasionally with mustard mixture. Serves 4. Serve with 1 cup steamed mixed vegetables and 1 whole-wheat dinner roll.

Nutritional Information: 484 Calories; 13g Fat (23.9% calories from fat); 30g Protein; 64g Carbohydrate; 11g Dietary Fiber; 63mg Cholesterol; 937mg Sodium.

STEPS FOR SPIRITUAL GROWTH

—— GOD'S WORD FOR YOUR LIFE

I have hidden your word in my heart that I might not sin against you.

Psalm 119:11

As you begin to make decisions based on what God's Word teaches you, you will want to memorize what He has promised to those who trust and follow Him. Second Peter 1:3 tells us that God "has given us everything we need for life and godliness through our knowledge of him" (emphasis added). The Bible provides instruction and encouragement for any area of life in which you may be struggling. If you are dealing with a particular emotion or traumatic life event—fear, discouragement, stress, financial upset, the death of a loved one, a relationship difficulty—you can search through a Bible concordance for Scripture passages that deal with that particular situation. Scripture provides great comfort to those who memorize it.

One of the promises of knowing and obeying God's Word is that it gives you wisdom, insight, and understanding above all worldly knowledge (see Psalm 119:97–104). Psalm 119:129–130 says, "Your statutes are wonderful; therefore I obey them. The unfolding of your words gives light; it gives understanding to the simple." Now that's a precious promise about guidance for life!

The Value of Scripture Memory

Scripture memory is an important part of the Christian life. There are four key reasons to memorize Scripture:

1. **TO HANDLE DIFFICULT SITUATIONS.** A heartfelt knowledge of God's Word will equip you to handle any situation that you might face. Declaring such truth as, "I can do everything through Christ" (see Philippians 4:13) and "he will never leave me or forsake me" (see Hebrews 13:5) will enable you to walk through situations with peace and courage.

2. **TO OVERCOME TEMPTATION.** Luke 4:1–13 describes how Jesus used Scripture to overcome His temptations in the desert (see also Matthew 4:1-11). Knowledge of Scripture and the strength that comes with the ability to use it are important parts of putting on the full armor of God in preparation for spiritual warfare (see Ephesians 6:10–18).

3. **TO GET GUIDANCE.** Psalm 119:105 states the Word of God "is a lamp to my feet and a light for my path." You learn to hide God's Word in your heart so His light will direct your decisions and actions throughout your day.

4. **TO TRANSFORM YOUR MIND.** "Do not conform any longer to the pattern of this world, but be transformed by the renewing of your mind" (Romans 12:2). Scripture memory allows you to replace a lie with the truth of God's Word. When Scripture becomes firmly settled in your memory, not only will your thoughts connect with God's thoughts, but you will also be able to honor God with small everyday decisions as well as big life-impacting ones. Scripture memorization is the key to making a permanent lifestyle change in your thought patterns, which brings balance to every other area of your life.

Scripture Memory Tips

- Write the verse down, saying it aloud as you write it.
- Read verses before and after the memory verse to get its context.
- Read the verse several times, emphasizing a different word each time.
- Connect the Scripture reference to the first few words.
- Locate patterns, phrases, or keywords.
- Apply the Scripture to circumstances you are now experiencing.
- Pray the verse, making it personal to your life and inserting your name as the recipient of the promise or teaching. (Try that with 1 Corinthians 10:13, inserting "me" and "I" for "you.")
- Review the verse every day until it becomes second nature to think those words whenever your circumstances match its message. The Holy Spirit will bring the verse to mind when you need it most if you decide to plant it in your memory.

Scripture Memorization Made Easy!

What is your learning style? Do you learn by hearing, by sight, or by doing?

If you learn by hearing—if you are an auditory learner—singing the Scripture memory verses, reading them aloud, or recording them and listening to your recording will be very helpful in the memorization process.

If you are a visual learner, writing the verses and repeatedly reading through them will cement them in your mind.

STEPS FOR SPIRITUAL GROWTH

If you learn by doing—if you are a tactile learner—creating motions for the words or using sign language will enable you to more easily recall the verse.

After determining your learning style, link your Scripture memory with a daily task, such as driving to work, walking on a treadmill, or eating lunch. Use these daily tasks as opportunities to memorize and review your verses.

Meals at home or out with friends can be used as a time to share the verse you are memorizing with those at your table. You could close your personal email messages by typing in your weekly memory verse. Or why not say your memory verse every time you brush your teeth or put on your shoes?

The purpose of Scripture memorization is to be able to apply God's words to your life. If you memorize Scripture using methods that connect with your particular learning style, you will find it easier to hide God's Word in your heart.

—— ESTABLISHING A QUIET TIME

Like all other components of the First Place for Health program, developing a live relationship with God is not a random act. You must intentionally seek God if you are to find Him! It's not that God plays hide-and-seek with you. He is always available to you. He invites you to come boldly into His presence. He reveals Himself to you in the pages of the Bible. And once you decide to earnestly seek Him, you are sure to find Him! When you delight in Him, your gracious God will give you the desires of your heart. Spending time getting to know God involves four basic elements: a priority, a plan, a place, and practice.

A Priority

You can successfully establish a quiet time with God by making this meeting a daily priority. This may require carving out time in your day so you have time and space for this new relationship you are cultivating. Often this will mean eliminating less important things so you will have time and space to meet with God. When speaking about Jesus, John the Baptist said, "He must become greater; I must become less" (John 3:30). You will undoubtedly find that to be true as well. What might you need to eliminate from your current schedule so that spending quality time with God can become a priority?

A Plan

Having made quiet time a priority, you will want to come up with a plan. This plan will include the time you have set aside to spend with God and a general outline of how you will spend your time in God's presence.

Elements you should consider incorporating into your quiet time include:

- Singing a song of praise
- Reading a daily selection in a devotional book or reading a psalm
- Using a systematic Scripture reading plan so you will be exposed to the whole truth of God's Word
- Completing your First Place for Health Bible study for that day
- Praying—silent, spoken, and written prayer
- Writing in your spiritual journal.

You will also want to make a list of the materials you will need to make your encounter with God more meaningful:

- A Bible
- Your First Place for Health Bible study
- Your prayer journal
- A pen and/or pencil
- A devotional book
- A Bible concordance
- A college-level dictionary
- A box of tissues (tears—both of sadness and joy—are often part of our quiet time with God!)

Think of how you would plan an important business meeting or social event, and then transfer that knowledge to your meeting time with God.

A Place

Having formulated a meeting-with-God plan, you will next need to create a meeting-with-God place. Of course, God is always with you; however, in order to have quality devotional time with Him, it is desirable that you find a comfortable meeting place. You will want to select a spot that is quiet and as distraction-free as possible. Meeting with God in the same place on a regular basis will help you remember what you are there for: to have an encounter with the true and living God!

Having selected the place, put the materials you have determined to use in your quiet time into a basket or on a nearby table or shelf. Now take the time to establish your personal quiet time with God. Tailor your quiet time to fit your needs—and the time you have allotted to spend with God. Although many people elect to meet with God early in the morning, for others afternoon or evening is best. There is no hard-and-fast rule about when your quiet time should be—the only essential thing is that you establish a quiet time!

Start with a small amount of time that you know you can devote yourself to daily. You can be confident that as you consistently spend time with God each day, the amount of time you can spend will increase as you are ready for the next level of your walk with God.

I will meet with God from _____ to _____ daily.

I plan to use that time with God to _____

_____

Supplies I will need to assemble include _____

_____

My meeting place with God will be _____

_____

Practice

After you have chosen the time and place to meet God each day and you have as-sembled your supplies, there are four easy steps for having a fruitful and worshipful time with the Lord.

STEP 1: Clear Your Heart and Mind

"Be still, and know that I am God" (Psalm 46:10). Begin your quiet time by reading the daily Bible selection from a devotional guide or a psalm. If you are new in your Christian walk, an excellent devotional guide to use is *Streams in the Desert* by L.B. Cowman. More mature Christians might benefit from My Utmost for His Highest by Oswald Chambers. Of course, you can use any devotional that has a strong emphasis on Scripture and prayer.

STEP 2: Read and Interact with Scripture

"I have hidden your word in my heart that I might not sin against you" (Psalm 119:11). As you open your Bible, ask the Holy Spirit to reveal something He knows you need for this day through the reading of His Word. Always try to find a nugget to encourage or direct you through the day. As you read the passage, pay special attention to the words and phrases the Holy Spirit brings to your attention. Some words may seem to resonate in your soul. You will want to spend time meditating on the passage, asking God what lesson He is teaching you.

After reading the Scripture passage over several times, ask yourself the following questions:

- In light of what I have read today, is there something I must now do? (Confess a sin? Claim a promise? Follow an example? Obey a command? Avoid a situation?)
- How should I respond to what I've read today?

STEP 3: Pray

"Be clear minded and self-controlled so that you can pray" (1 Peter 4:7). Spend time conversing with the Lord in prayer. Prayer is such an important part of First Place for Health that there is an entire section in this study devoted to the practice of prayer.

STEP 4: Praise

"Praise the LORD, O my soul, and forget not all his benefits" (Psalm 103:2). End your quiet time with a time of praise. Be sure to thank the Lord of heaven and warmth for choosing to spend time with you!

—— SHARING YOUR FAITH

Nothing is more effective in drawing someone to Jesus than sharing personal life experiences. People are more open to the good news of Jesus Christ when they see faith in action. Personal faith stories are simple and effective ways to share what Christ is doing in your life, because they show firsthand how Christ makes a difference.

Sharing your faith story has an added benefit: it builds you up in your faith, too! Is your experience in First Place for Health providing you opportunities to share with others what God is doing in your life? If you answered yes, then you have a personal faith story!

If you do not have a personal faith story, perhaps it is because you don't know Jesus Christ as your personal Lord and Savior. Read through "Steps to Becoming a Christian" (which is the next chapter) and begin today to give Christ first place in your life.

Creativity and preparation in using opportunities to share a word or story about Jesus is an important part of the Christian life. Is Jesus helping you in a special way? Are you achieving a level of success or peace that you haven't experienced in other attempts to lose weight, exercise regularly, or eat healthier? As people see you making changes and achieving success, they may ask you how you are doing it. How will—or do—you respond? Remember, your story is unique, and it may allow others to see what Christ is doing in your life. It may also help to bring Christ into the life of another person.

Personal Statements of Faith

First Place for Health gives you a great opportunity to communicate your faith and express what God is doing in your life. Be ready to use your own personal statement of faith whenever the opportunity presents itself. Personal statements of faith should be short and fit naturally into a conversation. They don't require or expect any action or response from the listener. The goal is not to get another person to change but simply to help you communicate who you are and what's important to you.

Here are some examples of short statements of faith that you might use when someone asks what you are doing to lose weight:

- "I've been meeting with a group at my church. We pray together, support each other, learn about nutrition, and study the Bible."
- "It's amazing how Bible study and prayer are helping me lose weight and eat healthier."
- "I've had a lot of support from a group I meet with at church."
- "I'm relying more on God to help me make changes in my lifestyle."

Begin keeping a list of your meaningful experiences as you go through the First Place for Health program. Also notice what is happening in the lives of others. Use the following questions to help you prepare short personal statements and stories of faith:

- What is God doing in your life physically, mentally, emotionally, and spiritually?
- How has your relationship with God changed? Is it more intimate or personal?
- How is prayer, Bible study, and/or the support of others helping you achieve your goals for a healthy weight and good nutrition?

Writing Your Personal Faith Story

Write a brief story about how God is working in your life through First Place for Health. Use your story to help you share with others what's happening in your life.

Use the following questions to help develop your story:

- Why did you join First Place for Health? What specific circumstances led you to a Christ-centered health and weight-loss program? What were you feeling when you joined?
- What was your relationship with Christ when you started First Place for Health? What is it now?
- Has your experience in First Place for Health changed your relationship with Christ? With yourself? With others?
- How has your relationship with Christ, prayer, Bible study, and group support made a difference in your life?
- What specific verse or passage of Scripture has made a difference in the way you view yourself or your relationship with Christ?
- What experiences have impacted your life since starting First Place for Health?
- In what ways is Christ working in your life today? In what ways is He meeting your needs?
- How has Christ worked in other members of your First Place for Health group?

Answer the above questions in a few sentences, and then use your answers to help you write your own short personal faith story.

MEMBER SURVEY

We would love to know more about you. Share this form with your leader.

Name _____   Birth date _____

Tell us about your family.

_____

_____

_____

_____

Would you like to receive more information   Yes   No
about our church?

What area of expertise would you be willing to share with our class?

_____

_____

Why did you join First Place for Health?

_____

_____

With notice, would you be willing to lead a Bible study   Yes   No
discussion one week?

Are you comfortable praying out loud? _____

Would you be willing to assist recording weights and/or   Yes   No
evaluating the Live It Trackers?

Any other comments:

_____

_____

PERSONAL WEIGHT AND MEASUREMENT RECORD

WEEK	WEIGHT	+ OR -	GOAL THIS SESSION	POUNDS TO GOAL
1				
2				
3				
4				
5				
6				
7				
8				
9				
10				
11				
12				

BEGINNING MEASUREMENTS

WAIST_____ HIPS_____ THIGHS_____ CHEST_____

ENDING MEASUREMENTS

WAIST_____ HIPS_____ THIGHS_____ CHEST_____

But I have raised you up for this very purpose, that I might show you my power and that my name might be proclaimed in all the earth. Exodus 9:16 NIV

Date: _____

Name: _____

Home Phone: _____

Cell Phone: _____

Email: _____

Personal Prayer Concerns

_____

_____

_____

_____

_____

_____

_____

_____

This form is for prayer requests that are personal to you and your journey in First Place for Health. Please complete and have it ready to turn in when you arrive at your group meeting.

PRAYER PARTNER WEEK 2

May he give you the desire of your heart and make all your plans
succeed. Psalm 20:4

Date: _____

Name: _____

Home Phone: _____

Cell Phone: _____

Email: _____

Personal Prayer Concerns

_____

_____

_____

_____

_____

_____

_____

This form is for prayer requests that are personal to you and your journey in First Place for Health. Please complete and have it ready to turn in when you arrive at your group meeting.

Love the LORD your God with all your heart and with all your soul and
with all your strength.
Deuteronomy 6:5

Date: _____

Name: _____

Home Phone: _____

Cell Phone: _____

Email: _____

Personal Prayer Concerns

_____

_____

_____

_____

_____

_____

_____

_____

This form is for prayer requests that are personal to you and your journey in First Place for Health. Please complete and have it ready to turn in when you arrive at your group meeting.

Put on the full armor of God so that you can take your stand against
the devil's schemes.
Ephesians 6:11

Date: _____

Name: _____

Home Phone: _____

Cell Phone: _____

Email: _____

Personal Prayer Concerns

_____

_____

_____

_____

_____

_____

_____

This form is for prayer requests that are personal to you and your journey in First Place for Health. Please complete and have it ready to turn in when you arrive at your group meeting.

Search me, O God, and know my heart; test me and know my anxious thoughts.
See if there is any offensive way in me, and lead me in the way everlasting.
Psalm 139:23-24

Date: _____

Name: _____

Home Phone: _____

Cell Phone: _____

Email: _____

Personal Prayer Concerns

_____

_____

_____

_____

_____

_____

_____

This form is for prayer requests that are personal to you and your journey in First Place for Health. Please complete and have it ready to turn in when you arrive at your group meeting.

Everyone born of God overcomes the world. This is the victory that has over-
come the world, even our faith. Who is it that overcomes the world? Only he
who believes that Jesus is the Son of God.
1 John 5:4-5

Date: _____

Name: _____

Home Phone: _____

Cell Phone: _____

Email: _____

Personal Prayer Concerns

_____

_____

_____

_____

_____

_____

_____

_____

This form is for prayer requests that are personal to you and your journey in First Place for Health. Please complete and have it ready to turn in when you arrive at your group meeting.

*Whether you turn to the right or to the left, your ears will hear a voice behind
you, saying, "This is the way; walk in it."*
Isaiah 30:21

Date: _____

Name: _____

Home Phone: _____

Cell Phone: _____

Email: _____

Personal Prayer Concerns

_____

_____

_____

_____

_____

_____

_____

_____

This form is for prayer requests that are personal to you and your journey in First Place for Health.
Please complete and have it ready to turn in when you arrive at your group meeting.

His divine power has given us everything we need for life and godliness through
our knowledge of him who called us by his own glory and goodness.
2 Peter 1:3

Date: _____

Name: _____

Home Phone: _____

Cell Phone: _____

Email: _____

Personal Prayer Concern

_____

_____

_____

_____

_____

_____

_____

This form is for prayer requests that are personal to you and your journey in First Place for Health. Please complete and have it ready to turn in when you arrive at your group meeting.

Date: _____

Name: _____

Home Phone: _____

Cell Phone: _____

Email: _____

Personal Prayer Concerns

_____

_____

_____

_____

_____

_____

_____

_____

This form is for prayer requests that are personal to you and your journey in First Place for Health. Please complete and have it ready to turn in when you arrive at your group meeting.

LIVE IT TRACKER

Name: _____

Date: _____ Week #: _____

My activity goal for next week:
○ None   ○ <30 min/day   ○ 30-60 min/day

loss / gain _____ Calorie Range: _____

My food goal for next week: _____

My week at a glance:
○ Great   ○ So-so   ○ Not so great

Activity level:
○ None   ○ <30 min/day   ○ 30-60 min/day

RECOMMENDED DAILY AMOUNT OF FOOD FROM EACH GROUP

GROUP	DAILY CALORIES							
	1300-1400	1500-1600	1700-1800	1900-2000	2100-2200	2300-2400	2500-2600	2700-2800
Fruits	1.5 – 2 c.	1.5 – 2 c.	1.5 – 2 c.	2 – 2.5 c.	2 – 2.5 c.	2.5 – 3.5 c.	3.5 – 4.5 c.	3.5 – 4.5 c.
Vegetables	1.5 – 2 c.	2 – 2.5 c.	2.5 – 3 c.	2.5 – 3 c.	3 – 3.5 c.	3.5 – 4.5 c.	4.5 – 5 c.	4.5 – 5 c.
Grains	5 oz eq.	5-6 oz eq.	6-7 oz eq.	6-7 oz eq.	7-8 oz eq.	8-9 oz eq.	9-10 oz eq.	10-11 oz eq.
Dairy	2-3 c.	3 c.	3 c.	3 c.	3 c.	3 c.	3 c.	3 c.
Protein	4 oz eq.	5 oz eq.	5-5.5 oz eq.	5.5-6.5 oz eq.	6.5-7 oz eq.	7-7.5 oz eq.	7-7.5 oz eq.	7.5-8 oz eq.
Healthy Oils & Other Fats	4 tsp.	5 tsp.	5 tsp.	6 tsp.	6 tsp.	7 tsp.	8 tsp.	8 tsp.
Water & Super Beverages*	Women: 9 c. Men: 13 c.	Women: 9 c. Men: 13 c.	Women: 9 c. Men: 13 c.	Women: 9 c. Men: 13 c.	Women: 9 c. Men: 13 c.	Women: 9 c. Men: 13 c.	Women: 9 c. Men: 13 c.	Women: 9 c. Men: 13 c.

*May count up to 3 cups caffeinated tea or coffee toward goal

DAILY FOOD GROUP TRACKER

GROUP	FRUITS	VEGETABLES	GRAINS	PROTEIN	DAIRY	HEALTHY OILS & OTHER FATS	WATER & SUPER BEVERAGES
1 Estimate Total							
2 Estimate Total							
3 Estimate Total							
4 Estimate Total							
5 Estimate Total							
6 Estimate Total							
7 Estimate Total							

FOOD CHOICES   DAY ❶

Breakfast: _____
Lunch: _____
Dinner: _____
Snacks: _____

PHYSICAL ACTIVITY   steps/miles/minutes: _____
description: _____

SPIRITUAL ACTIVITY
description: _____

FOOD CHOICES   DAY ❷

Breakfast: _____

Lunch: _____

Dinner: _____

Snacks: _____

PHYSICAL ACTIVITY   steps/miles/minutes:

description: _____

SPIRITUAL ACTIVITY

description: _____

FOOD CHOICES   DAY ❸

Breakfast: _____

Lunch: _____

Dinner: _____

Snacks: _____

PHYSICAL ACTIVITY   steps/miles/minutes:

description: _____

SPIRITUAL ACTIVITY

description: _____

FOOD CHOICES   DAY ❹

Breakfast: _____

Lunch: _____

Dinner: _____

Snacks: _____

PHYSICAL ACTIVITY   steps/miles/minutes:

description: _____

SPIRITUAL ACTIVITY

description: _____

FOOD CHOICES   DAY ❺

Breakfast: _____

Lunch: _____

Dinner: _____

Snacks: _____

PHYSICAL ACTIVITY   steps/miles/minutes:

description: _____

SPIRITUAL ACTIVITY

description: _____

FOOD CHOICES   DAY ❻

Breakfast: _____

Lunch: _____

Dinner: _____

Snacks: _____

PHYSICAL ACTIVITY   steps/miles/minutes:

description: _____

SPIRITUAL ACTIVITY

description: _____

FOOD CHOICES   DAY ❼

Breakfast: _____

Lunch: _____

Dinner: _____

Snacks: _____

PHYSICAL ACTIVITY   steps/miles/minutes:

description: _____

SPIRITUAL ACTIVITY

description: _____

LIVE IT TRACKER

Name: _____

Date: _____ Week #: _____

My activity goal for next week:
○ None ○ <30 min/day ○ 30-60 min/day

loss / gain _____ Calorie Range: _____

My week at a glance:
○ Great ○ So-so ○ Not so great

My food goal for next week: _____
_____

Activity level:
○ None ○ <30 min/day ○ 30-60 min/day

RECOMMENDED DAILY AMOUNT OF FOOD FROM EACH GROUP

GROUP	DAILY CALORIES							
	1300-1400	1500-1600	1700-1800	1900-2000	2100-2200	2300-2400	2500-2600	2700-2800
Fruits	1.5 – 2 c.	1.5 – 2 c.	1.5 – 2 c.	2 – 2.5 c.	2 – 2.5 c.	2.5 – 3.5 c.	3.5 – 4.5 c.	3.5 – 4.5 c.
Vegetables	1.5 – 2 c.	2 – 2.5 c.	2.5 – 3 c.	2.5 – 3 c.	3 – 3.5 c.	3.5 – 4.5 c.	4.5 – 5 c.	4.5 – 5 c.
Grains	5 oz eq.	5-6 oz eq.	6-7 oz eq.	6-7 oz eq.	7-8 oz eq.	8-9 oz eq.	9-10 oz eq.	10-11 oz eq.
Dairy	2-3 c.	3 c.	3 c.	3 c.	3 c.	3 c.	3 c.	3 c.
Protein	4 oz eq.	5 oz eq.	5-5.5 oz eq.	5.5-6.5 oz eq.	6.5-7 oz eq.	7-7.5 oz eq.	7-7.5 oz eq.	7.5-8 oz eq.
Healthy Oils & Other Fats	4 tsp.	5 tsp.	5 tsp.	6 tsp.	6 tsp.	7 tsp.	8 tsp.	8 tsp.
Water & Super Beverages*	Women: 9 c. Men: 13 c.	Women: 9 c. Men: 13 c.	Women: 9 c. Men: 13 c.	Women: 9 c. Men: 13 c.	Women: 9 c. Men: 13 c.	Women: 9 c. Men: 13 c.	Women: 9 c. Men: 13 c.	Women: 9 c. Men: 13 c.

*May count up to 3 cups caffeinated tea or coffee toward goal

DAILY FOOD GROUP TRACKER

GROUP	FRUITS	VEGETABLES	GRAINS	PROTEIN	DAIRY	HEALTHY OILS & OTHER FATS	WATER & SUPER BEVERAGES
1 Estimate Total							
2 Estimate Total							
3 Estimate Total							
4 Estimate Total							
5 Estimate Total							
6 Estimate Total							
7 Estimate Total							

FOOD CHOICES

DAY ❶

Breakfast: _____
Lunch: _____
Dinner: _____
Snacks: _____

PHYSICAL ACTIVITY steps/miles/minutes: _____

description: _____
_____

SPIRITUAL ACTIVITY

description: _____
_____

FOOD CHOICES   DAY ❷

Breakfast: _____

Lunch: _____

Dinner: _____

Snacks: _____

PHYSICAL ACTIVITY steps/miles/minutes: _____	SPIRITUAL ACTIVITY
description: _____	description: _____

FOOD CHOICES   DAY ❸

Breakfast: _____

Lunch: _____

Dinner: _____

Snacks: _____

PHYSICAL ACTIVITY steps/miles/minutes: _____	SPIRITUAL ACTIVITY
description: _____	description: _____

FOOD CHOICES   DAY ❹

Breakfast: _____

Lunch: _____

Dinner: _____

Snacks: _____

PHYSICAL ACTIVITY steps/miles/minutes: _____	SPIRITUAL ACTIVITY
description: _____	description: _____

FOOD CHOICES   DAY ❺

Breakfast: _____

Lunch: _____

Dinner: _____

Snacks: _____

PHYSICAL ACTIVITY steps/miles/minutes: _____	SPIRITUAL ACTIVITY
description: _____	description: _____

FOOD CHOICES   DAY ❻

Breakfast: _____

Lunch: _____

Dinner: _____

Snacks: _____

PHYSICAL ACTIVITY steps/miles/minutes: _____	SPIRITUAL ACTIVITY
description: _____	description: _____

FOOD CHOICES   DAY ❼

Breakfast: _____

Lunch: _____

Dinner: _____

Snacks: _____

PHYSICAL ACTIVITY steps/miles/minutes: _____	SPIRITUAL ACTIVITY
description: _____	description: _____

LIVE IT TRACKER

Name: _____

Date: _____ Week #: _____

My activity goal for next week:
○ None   ○ <30 min/day   ○ 30-60 min/day

loss / gain _____ Calorie Range: _____

My food goal for next week: _____
_____

My week at a glance:
○ Great   ○ So-so   ○ Not so great

Activity level:
○ None   ○ <30 min/day   ○ 30-60 min/day

RECOMMENDED DAILY AMOUNT OF FOOD FROM EACH GROUP

GROUP	DAILY CALORIES							
	1300-1400	1500-1600	1700-1800	1900-2000	2100-2200	2300-2400	2500-2600	2700-2800
Fruits	1.5 – 2 c.	1.5 – 2 c.	1.5 – 2 c.	2 – 2.5 c.	2 – 2.5 c.	2.5 – 3.5 c.	3.5 – 4.5 c.	3.5 – 4.5 c.
Vegetables	1.5 – 2 c.	2 – 2.5 c.	2.5 – 3 c.	2.5 – 3 c.	3 – 3.5 c.	3.5 – 4.5 c.	4.5 – 5 c.	4.5 – 5 c.
Grains	5 oz eq.	5-6 oz eq.	6-7 oz eq.	6-7 oz eq.	7-8 oz eq.	8-9 oz eq.	9-10 oz eq.	10-11 oz eq.
Dairy	2-3 c.	3 c.	3 c.	3 c.	3 c.	3 c.	3 c.	3 c.
Protein	4 oz eq.	5 oz eq.	5-5.5 oz eq.	5.5-6.5 oz eq.	6.5-7 oz eq.	7-7.5 oz eq.	7-7.5 oz eq.	7.5-8 oz eq.
Healthy Oils & Other Fats	4 tsp.	5 tsp.	5 tsp.	6 tsp.	6 tsp.	7 tsp.	8 tsp.	8 tsp.
Water & Super Beverages*	Women: 9 c. Men: 13 c.	Women: 9 c. Men: 13 c.	Women: 9 c. Men: 13 c.	Women: 9 c. Men: 13 c.	Women: 9 c. Men: 13 c.	Women: 9 c. Men: 13 c.	Women: 9 c. Men: 13 c.	Women: 9 c. Men: 13 c.

*May count up to 3 cups caffeinated tea or coffee toward goal

DAILY FOOD GROUP TRACKER

GROUP	FRUITS	VEGETABLES	GRAINS	PROTEIN	DAIRY	HEALTHY OILS & OTHER FATS	WATER & SUPER BEVERAGES
❶ Estimate Total							
❷ Estimate Total							
❸ Estimate Total							
❹ Estimate Total							
❺ Estimate Total							
❻ Estimate Total							
❼ Estimate Total							

FOOD CHOICES   DAY ❶

Breakfast: _____
Lunch: _____
Dinner: _____
Snacks: _____

PHYSICAL ACTIVITY   steps/miles/minutes: _____

description: _____

SPIRITUAL ACTIVITY

description: _____

FOOD CHOICES   DAY ➋

Breakfast: _____
Lunch: _____
Dinner: _____
Snacks: _____

PHYSICAL ACTIVITY   steps/miles/minutes: _____   ### SPIRITUAL ACTIVITY

description: _____   description: _____

FOOD CHOICES   DAY ➌

Breakfast: _____
Lunch: _____
Dinner: _____
Snacks: _____

PHYSICAL ACTIVITY   steps/miles/minutes: _____   ### SPIRITUAL ACTIVITY

description: _____   description: _____

FOOD CHOICES   DAY ➍

Breakfast: _____
Lunch: _____
Dinner: _____
Snacks: _____

PHYSICAL ACTIVITY   steps/miles/minutes: _____   ### SPIRITUAL ACTIVITY

description: _____   description: _____

FOOD CHOICES   DAY ➎

Breakfast: _____
Lunch: _____
Dinner: _____
Snacks: _____

PHYSICAL ACTIVITY   steps/miles/minutes: _____   ### SPIRITUAL ACTIVITY

description: _____   description: _____

FOOD CHOICES   DAY ➏

Breakfast: _____
Lunch: _____
Dinner: _____
Snacks: _____

PHYSICAL ACTIVITY   steps/miles/minutes: _____   ### SPIRITUAL ACTIVITY

description: _____   description: _____

FOOD CHOICES   DAY ➐

Breakfast: _____
Lunch: _____
Dinner: _____
Snacks: _____

PHYSICAL ACTIVITY   steps/miles/minutes: _____   ### SPIRITUAL ACTIVITY

description: _____   description: _____

LIVE IT TRACKER

Name: _____

Date: _____ Week #: _____

My activity goal for next week:
○ None ○ <30 min/day ○ 30-60 min/day

loss / gain _____ Calorie Range: _____

My week at a glance:
○ Great ○ So-so ○ Not so great

My food goal for next week: _____

Activity level:
○ None ○ <30 min/day ○ 30-60 min/day

RECOMMENDED DAILY AMOUNT OF FOOD FROM EACH GROUP

GROUP	DAILY CALORIES							
	1300-1400	1500-1600	1700-1800	1900-2000	2100-2200	2300-2400	2500-2600	2700-2800
Fruits	1.5 – 2 c.	1.5 – 2 c.	1.5 – 2 c.	2 – 2.5 c.	2 – 2.5 c.	2.5 – 3.5 c.	3.5 – 4.5 c.	3.5 – 4.5 c.
Vegetables	1.5 – 2 c.	2 – 2.5 c.	2.5 – 3 c.	2.5 – 3 c.	3 – 3.5 c.	3.5 – 4.5 c.	4.5 – 5 c.	4.5 – 5 c.
Grains	5 oz eq.	5-6 oz eq.	6-7 oz eq.	6-7 oz eq.	7-8 oz eq.	8-9 oz eq.	9-10 oz eq.	10-11 oz eq.
Dairy	2-3 c.	3 c.	3 c.	3 c.	3 c.	3 c.	3 c.	3 c.
Protein	4 oz eq.	5 oz eq.	5-5.5 oz eq.	5.5-6.5 oz eq.	6.5-7 oz eq.	7-7.5 oz eq.	7-7.5 oz eq.	7.5-8 oz eq.
Healthy Oils & Other Fats	4 tsp.	5 tsp.	5 tsp.	6 tsp.	6 tsp.	7 tsp.	8 tsp.	8 tsp.
Water & Super Beverages*	Women: 9 c. Men: 13 c.	Women: 9 c. Men: 13 c.	Women: 9 c. Men: 13 c.	Women: 9 c. Men: 13 c.	Women: 9 c. Men: 13 c.	Women: 9 c. Men: 13 c.	Women: 9 c. Men: 13 c.	Women: 9 c. Men: 13 c.

*May count up to 3 cups caffeinated tea or coffee toward goal

DAILY FOOD GROUP TRACKER

GROUP	FRUITS	VEGETABLES	GRAINS	PROTEIN	DAIRY	HEALTHY OILS & OTHER FATS	WATER & SUPER BEVERAGES
1 Estimate Total							
2 Estimate Total							
3 Estimate Total							
4 Estimate Total							
5 Estimate Total							
6 Estimate Total							
7 Estimate Total							

FOOD CHOICES   DAY ❶

Breakfast: _____
Lunch: _____
Dinner: _____
Snacks: _____

PHYSICAL ACTIVITY steps/miles/minutes: _____

description: _____

SPIRITUAL ACTIVITY

description: _____

FOOD CHOICES · DAY 2

Breakfast: _____
Lunch: _____
Dinner: _____
Snacks: _____

PHYSICAL ACTIVITY   steps/miles/minutes: _____

description: _____

SPIRITUAL ACTIVITY

description: _____

FOOD CHOICES · DAY 3

Breakfast: _____
Lunch: _____
Dinner: _____
Snacks: _____

PHYSICAL ACTIVITY   steps/miles/minutes: _____

description: _____

SPIRITUAL ACTIVITY

description: _____

FOOD CHOICES · DAY 4

Breakfast: _____
Lunch: _____
Dinner: _____
Snacks: _____

PHYSICAL ACTIVITY   steps/miles/minutes: _____

description: _____

SPIRITUAL ACTIVITY

description: _____

FOOD CHOICES · DAY 5

Breakfast: _____
Lunch: _____
Dinner: _____
Snacks: _____

PHYSICAL ACTIVITY   steps/miles/minutes: _____

description: _____

SPIRITUAL ACTIVITY

description: _____

FOOD CHOICES · DAY 6

Breakfast: _____
Lunch: _____
Dinner: _____
Snacks: _____

PHYSICAL ACTIVITY   steps/miles/minutes: _____

description: _____

SPIRITUAL ACTIVITY

description: _____

FOOD CHOICES · DAY 7

Breakfast: _____
Lunch: _____
Dinner: _____
Snacks: _____

PHYSICAL ACTIVITY   steps/miles/minutes: _____

description: _____

SPIRITUAL ACTIVITY

description: _____

LIVE IT TRACKER

Name: _____

My activity goal for next week:
○ None   ○ <30 min/day   ○ 30-60 min/day

My food goal for next week: _____
_____

Date: _____ Week #: _____

loss / gain _____ Calorie Range: _____

My week at a glance:
○ Great   ○ So-so   ○ Not so great

Activity level:
○ None   ○ <30 min/day   ○ 30-60 min/day

RECOMMENDED DAILY AMOUNT OF FOOD FROM EACH GROUP

GROUP	DAILY CALORIES							
	1300-1400	1500-1600	1700-1800	1900-2000	2100-2200	2300-2400	2500-2600	2700-2800
Fruits	1.5 – 2 c.	1.5 – 2 c.	1.5 – 2 c.	2 – 2.5 c.	2 – 2.5 c.	2.5 – 3.5 c.	3.5 – 4.5 c.	3.5 – 4.5 c.
Vegetables	1.5 – 2 c.	2 – 2.5 c.	2.5 – 3 c.	2.5 – 3 c.	3 – 3.5 c.	3.5 – 4.5 c.	4.5 – 5 c.	4.5 – 5 c.
Grains	5 oz eq.	5-6 oz eq.	6-7 oz eq.	6-7 oz eq.	7-8 oz eq.	8-9 oz eq.	9-10 oz eq.	10-11 oz eq.
Dairy	2-3 c.	3 c.	3 c.	3 c.	3 c.	3 c.	3 c.	3 c.
Protein	4 oz eq.	5 oz eq.	5-5.5 oz eq.	5.5-6.5 oz eq.	6.5-7 oz eq.	7-7.5 oz eq.	7-7.5 oz eq.	7.5-8 oz eq.
Healthy Oils & Other Fats	4 tsp.	5 tsp.	5 tsp.	6 tsp.	6 tsp.	7 tsp.	8 tsp.	8 tsp.
Water & Super Beverages*	Women: 9 c. Men: 13 c.	Women: 9 c. Men: 13 c.	Women: 9 c. Men: 13 c.	Women: 9 c. Men: 13 c.	Women: 9 c. Men: 13 c.	Women: 9 c. Men: 13 c.	Women: 9 c. Men: 13 c.	Women: 9 c. Men: 13 c.

*May count up to 3 cups caffeinated tea or coffee toward goal

DAILY FOOD GROUP TRACKER

GROUP	FRUITS	VEGETABLES	GRAINS	PROTEIN	DAIRY	HEALTHY OILS & OTHER FATS	WATER & SUPER BEVERAGES
1 Estimate Total							
2 Estimate Total							
3 Estimate Total							
4 Estimate Total							
5 Estimate Total							
6 Estimate Total							
7 Estimate Total							

FOOD CHOICES   DAY ❶

Breakfast: _____
Lunch: _____
Dinner: _____
Snacks: _____

PHYSICAL ACTIVITY   steps/miles/minutes: _____

description: _____

SPIRITUAL ACTIVITY

description: _____

FOOD CHOICES   DAY 2

Breakfast: _____
Lunch: _____
Dinner: _____
Snacks: _____

PHYSICAL ACTIVITY   steps/miles/minutes: _____   ## SPIRITUAL ACTIVITY

description: _____   description: _____

FOOD CHOICES   DAY 3

Breakfast: _____
Lunch: _____
Dinner: _____
Snacks: _____

PHYSICAL ACTIVITY   steps/miles/minutes: _____   ## SPIRITUAL ACTIVITY

description: _____   description: _____

FOOD CHOICES   DAY 4

Breakfast: _____
Lunch: _____
Dinner: _____
Snacks: _____

PHYSICAL ACTIVITY   steps/miles/minutes: _____   ## SPIRITUAL ACTIVITY

description: _____   description: _____

FOOD CHOICES   DAY 5

Breakfast: _____
Lunch: _____
Dinner: _____
Snacks: _____

PHYSICAL ACTIVITY   steps/miles/minutes: _____   ## SPIRITUAL ACTIVITY

description: _____   description: _____

FOOD CHOICES   DAY 6

Breakfast: _____
Lunch: _____
Dinner: _____
Snacks: _____

PHYSICAL ACTIVITY   steps/miles/minutes: _____   ## SPIRITUAL ACTIVITY

description: _____   description: _____

FOOD CHOICES   DAY 7

Breakfast: _____
Lunch: _____
Dinner: _____
Snacks: _____

PHYSICAL ACTIVITY   steps/miles/minutes: _____   ## SPIRITUAL ACTIVITY

description: _____   description: _____

LIVE IT TRACKER

Name: _____

Date: _____ Week #: _____

My activity goal for next week:
○ None ○ <30 min/day ○ 30-60 min/day

loss / gain _____ Calorie Range: _____

My food goal for next week: _____
_____

My week at a glance:
○ Great ○ So-so ○ Not so great

Activity level:
○ None ○ <30 min/day ○ 30-60 min/day

RECOMMENDED DAILY AMOUNT OF FOOD FROM EACH GROUP

GROUP	DAILY CALORIES							
......	1300-1400	1500-1600	1700-1800	1900-2000	2100-2200	2300-2400	2500-2600	2700-2800
Fruits	1.5 – 2 c.	1.5 – 2 c.	1.5 – 2 c.	2 – 2.5 c.	2 – 2.5 c.	2.5 – 3.5 c.	3.5 – 4.5 c.	3.5 – 4.5 c.
Vegetables	1.5 – 2 c.	2 – 2.5 c.	2.5 – 3 c.	2.5 – 3 c.	3 – 3.5 c.	3.5 – 4.5 c.	4.5 – 5 c.	4.5 – 5 c.
Grains	5 oz eq.	5-6 oz eq.	6-7 oz eq.	6-7 oz eq.	7-8 oz eq.	8-9 oz eq.	9-10 oz eq.	10-11 oz eq.
Dairy	2-3 c.	3 c.	3 c.	3 c.	3 c.	3 c.	3 c.	3 c.
Protein	4 oz eq.	5 oz eq.	5-5.5 oz eq.	5.5-6.5 oz eq.	6.5-7 oz eq.	7-7.5 oz eq.	7-7.5 oz eq.	7.5-8 oz eq.
Healthy Oils & Other Fats	4 tsp.	5 tsp.	5 tsp.	6 tsp.	6 tsp.	7 tsp.	8 tsp.	8 tsp.
Water & Super Beverages*	Women: 9 c. Men: 13 c.	Women: 9 c. Men: 13 c.	Women: 9 c. Men: 13 c.	Women: 9 c. Men: 13 c.	Women: 9 c. Men: 13 c.	Women: 9 c. Men: 13 c.	Women: 9 c. Men: 13 c.	Women: 9 c. Men: 13 c.

*May count up to 3 cups caffeinated tea or coffee toward goal

DAILY FOOD GROUP TRACKER

GROUP	FRUITS	VEGETABLES	GRAINS	PROTEIN	DAIRY	HEALTHY OILS & OTHER FATS	WATER & SUPER BEVERAGES
1 Estimate Total							
2 Estimate Total							
3 Estimate Total							
4 Estimate Total							
5 Estimate Total							
6 Estimate Total							
7 Estimate Total							

FOOD CHOICES   DAY ❶

Breakfast: _____
Lunch: _____
Dinner: _____
Snacks: _____

PHYSICAL ACTIVITY   steps/miles/minutes: _____

description: _____

SPIRITUAL ACTIVITY

description: _____

FOOD CHOICES   DAY 2

Breakfast: ....

Lunch: ....

Dinner: ....

Snacks: ....

PHYSICAL ACTIVITY   steps/miles/minutes: ....   ### SPIRITUAL ACTIVITY

description: ....   description: ....

FOOD CHOICES   DAY 3

Breakfast: ....

Lunch: ....

Dinner: ....

Snacks: ....

PHYSICAL ACTIVITY   steps/miles/minutes: ....   ### SPIRITUAL ACTIVITY

description: ....   description: ....

FOOD CHOICES   DAY 4

Breakfast: ....

Lunch: ....

Dinner: ....

Snacks: ....

PHYSICAL ACTIVITY   steps/miles/minutes: ....   ### SPIRITUAL ACTIVITY

description: ....   description: ....

FOOD CHOICES   DAY 5

Breakfast: ....

Lunch: ....

Dinner: ....

Snacks: ....

PHYSICAL ACTIVITY   steps/miles/minutes: ....   ### SPIRITUAL ACTIVITY

description: ....   description: ....

FOOD CHOICES   DAY 6

Breakfast: ....

Lunch: ....

Dinner: ....

Snacks: ....

PHYSICAL ACTIVITY   steps/miles/minutes: ....   ### SPIRITUAL ACTIVITY

description: ....   description: ....

FOOD CHOICES   DAY 7

Breakfast: ....

Lunch: ....

Dinner: ....

Snacks: ....

PHYSICAL ACTIVITY   steps/miles/minutes: ....   ### SPIRITUAL ACTIVITY

description: ....   description: ....

LIVE IT TRACKER

Name: _____

Date: _____ Week #: _____

My activity goal for next week:
○ None   ○ <30 min/day   ○ 30-60 min/day

loss / gain _____ Calorie Range: _____

My week at a glance:
○ Great   ○ So-so   ○ Not so great

My food goal for next week: _____

Activity level:
○ None   ○ <30 min/day   ○ 30-60 min/day

RECOMMENDED DAILY AMOUNT OF FOOD FROM EACH GROUP

GROUP	DAILY CALORIES							
	1300-1400	1500-1600	1700-1800	1900-2000	2100-2200	2300-2400	2500-2600	2700-2800
Fruits	1.5 – 2 c.	1.5 – 2 c.	1.5 – 2 c.	2 – 2.5 c.	2 – 2.5 c.	2.5 – 3.5 c.	3.5 – 4.5 c.	3.5 – 4.5 c.
Vegetables	1.5 – 2 c.	2 – 2.5 c.	2.5 – 3 c.	2.5 – 3 c.	3 – 3.5 c.	3.5 – 4.5 c..	4.5 – 5 c.	4.5 – 5 c.
Grains	5 oz eq.	5-6 oz eq.	6-7 oz eq.	6-7 oz eq.	7-8 oz eq.	8-9 oz eq.	9-10 oz eq.	10-11 oz eq.
Dairy	2-3 c.	3 c.	3 c.	3 c.	3 c.	3 c.	3 c.	3 c.
Protein	4 oz eq.	5 oz eq.	5-5.5 oz eq.	5.5-6.5 oz eq.	6.5-7 oz eq.	7-7.5 oz eq.	7-7.5 oz eq.	7.5-8 oz eq.
Healthy Oils & Other Fats	4 tsp.	5 tsp.	5 tsp.	6 tsp.	6 tsp.	7 tsp.	8 tsp.	8 tsp.
Water & Super Beverages*	Women: 9 c. Men: 13 c.	Women: 9 c. Men: 13 c.	Women: 9 c. Men: 13 c.	Women: 9 c. Men: 13 c.	Women: 9 c. Men: 13 c.	Women: 9 c. Men: 13 c.	Women: 9 c. Men: 13 c.	Women: 9 c. Men: 13 c.

*May count up to 3 cups caffeinated tea or coffee toward goal

DAILY FOOD GROUP TRACKER

GROUP	FRUITS	VEGETABLES	GRAINS	PROTEIN	DAIRY	HEALTHY OILS & OTHER FATS	WATER & SUPER BEVERAGES
1 Estimate Total							
2 Estimate Total							
3 Estimate Total							
4 Estimate Total							
5 Estimate Total							
6 Estimate Total							
7 Estimate Total							

FOOD CHOICES   DAY ❶

Breakfast: _____
Lunch: _____
Dinner: _____
Snacks: _____

PHYSICAL ACTIVITY   steps/miles/minutes: _____

description: _____

SPIRITUAL ACTIVITY

description: _____

FOOD CHOICES   DAY ❷

Breakfast: _____

Lunch: _____

Dinner: _____

Snacks: _____

PHYSICAL ACTIVITY   steps/miles/minutes: _____ | SPIRITUAL ACTIVITY

description: _____ | description: _____

_____ | _____

FOOD CHOICES   DAY ❸

Breakfast: _____

Lunch: _____

Dinner: _____

Snacks: _____

PHYSICAL ACTIVITY   steps/miles/minutes: _____ | SPIRITUAL ACTIVITY

description: _____ | description: _____

_____ | _____

FOOD CHOICES   DAY ❹

Breakfast: _____

Lunch: _____

Dinner: _____

Snacks: _____

PHYSICAL ACTIVITY   steps/miles/minutes: _____ | SPIRITUAL ACTIVITY

description: _____ | description: _____

_____ | _____

FOOD CHOICES   DAY ❺

Breakfast: _____

Lunch: _____

Dinner: _____

Snacks: _____

PHYSICAL ACTIVITY   steps/miles/minutes: _____ | SPIRITUAL ACTIVITY

description: _____ | description: _____

_____ | _____

FOOD CHOICES   DAY ❻

Breakfast: _____

Lunch: _____

Dinner: _____

Snacks: _____

PHYSICAL ACTIVITY   steps/miles/minutes: _____ | SPIRITUAL ACTIVITY

description: _____ | description: _____

_____ | _____

FOOD CHOICES   DAY ❼

Breakfast: _____

Lunch: _____

Dinner: _____

Snacks: _____

PHYSICAL ACTIVITY   steps/miles/minutes: _____ | SPIRITUAL ACTIVITY

description: _____ | description: _____

_____ | _____

Name: _____

My activity goal for next week:
○ None   ○ <30 min/day   ○ 30-60 min/day

My food goal for next week: _____
_____

Date: _____ Week #: _____

loss / gain _____ Calorie Range: _____

My week at a glance:
○ Great   ○ So-so   ○ Not so great

Activity level:
○ None   ○ <30 min/day   ○ 30-60 min/day

RECOMMENDED DAILY AMOUNT OF FOOD FROM EACH GROUP

GROUP	DAILY CALORIES							
	1300-1400	1500-1600	1700-1800	1900-2000	2100-2200	2300-2400	2500-2600	2700-2800
Fruits	1.5 – 2 c.	1.5 – 2 c.	1.5 – 2 c.	2 – 2.5 c.	2 – 2.5 c.	2.5 – 3.5 c.	3.5 – 4.5 c.	3.5 – 4.5 c.
Vegetables	1.5 – 2 c.	2 – 2.5 c.	2.5 – 3 c.	2.5 – 3 c.	3 – 3.5 c.	3.5 – 4.5 c.	4.5 – 5 c.	4.5 – 5 c.
Grains	5 oz eq.	5-6 oz eq.	6-7 oz eq.	6-7 oz eq.	7-8 oz eq.	8-9 oz eq.	9-10 oz eq.	10-11 oz eq.
Dairy	2-3 c.	3 c.	3 c.	3 c.	3 c.	3 c.	3 c.	3 c.
Protein	4 oz eq.	5 oz eq.	5-5.5 oz eq.	5.5-6.5 oz eq.	6.5-7 oz eq.	7-7.5 oz eq.	7-7.5 oz eq.	7.5-8 oz eq.
Healthy Oils & Other Fats	4 tsp.	5 tsp.	5 tsp.	6 tsp.	6 tsp.	7 tsp.	8 tsp.	8 tsp.
Water & Super Beverages*	Women: 9 c. Men: 13 c.	Women: 9 c. Men: 13 c.	Women: 9 c. Men: 13 c.	Women: 9 c. Men: 13 c.	Women: 9 c. Men: 13 c.	Women: 9 c. Men: 13 c.	Women: 9 c. Men: 13 c.	Women: 9 c. Men: 13 c.

*May count up to 3 cups caffeinated tea or coffee toward goal

DAILY FOOD GROUP TRACKER

GROUP	FRUITS	VEGETABLES	GRAINS	PROTEIN	DAIRY	HEALTHY OILS & OTHER FATS	WATER & SUPER BEVERAGES
1 Estimate Total							
2 Estimate Total							
3 Estimate Total							
4 Estimate Total							
5 Estimate Total							
6 Estimate Total							
7 Estimate Total							

FOOD CHOICES   DAY ❶

Breakfast: _____
Lunch: _____
Dinner: _____
Snacks: _____

PHYSICAL ACTIVITY   steps/miles/minutes: _____

description: _____
_____

SPIRITUAL ACTIVITY

description: _____
_____

FOOD CHOICES

DAY 2

Breakfast: _____

Lunch: _____

Dinner: _____

Snacks: _____

PHYSICAL ACTIVITY   steps/miles/minutes: _____

description: _____

SPIRITUAL ACTIVITY

description: _____

FOOD CHOICES

DAY 3

Breakfast: _____

Lunch: _____

Dinner: _____

Snacks: _____

PHYSICAL ACTIVITY   steps/miles/minutes: _____

description: _____

SPIRITUAL ACTIVITY

description: _____

FOOD CHOICES

DAY 4

Breakfast: _____

Lunch: _____

Dinner: _____

Snacks: _____

PHYSICAL ACTIVITY   steps/miles/minutes: _____

description: _____

SPIRITUAL ACTIVITY

description: _____

FOOD CHOICES

DAY 5

Breakfast: _____

Lunch: _____

Dinner: _____

Snacks: _____

PHYSICAL ACTIVITY   steps/miles/minutes: _____

description: _____

SPIRITUAL ACTIVITY

description: _____

FOOD CHOICES

DAY 6

Breakfast: _____

Lunch: _____

Dinner: _____

Snacks: _____

PHYSICAL ACTIVITY   steps/miles/minutes: _____

description: _____

SPIRITUAL ACTIVITY

description: _____

FOOD CHOICES

DAY 7

Breakfast: _____

Lunch: _____

Dinner: _____

Snacks: _____

PHYSICAL ACTIVITY   steps/miles/minutes: _____

description: _____

SPIRITUAL ACTIVITY

description: _____

Name: _____

Date: _____ Week #: _____

My activity goal for next week:
○ None   ○ <30 min/day   ○ 30-60 min/day

loss / gain _____ Calorie Range: _____

My week at a glance:
○ Great   ○ So-so   ○ Not so great

My food goal for next week: _____

Activity level:
○ None ○ <30 min/day ○ 30-60 min/day

RECOMMENDED DAILY AMOUNT OF FOOD FROM EACH GROUP

GROUP	DAILY CALORIES							
	1300-1400	1500-1600	1700-1800	1900-2000	2100-2200	2300-2400	2500-2600	2700-2800
Fruits	1.5 – 2 c.	1.5 – 2 c.	1.5 – 2 c.	2 – 2.5 c.	2 – 2.5 c.	2.5 – 3.5 c.	3.5 – 4.5 c.	3.5 – 4.5 c.
Vegetables	1.5 – 2 c.	2 – 2.5 c.	2.5 – 3 c.	2.5 – 3 c.	3 – 3.5 c.	3.5 – 4.5 c.	4.5 – 5 c.	4.5 – 5 c.
Grains	5 oz eq.	5-6 oz eq.	6-7 oz eq.	6-7 oz eq.	7-8 oz eq.	8-9 oz eq.	9-10 oz eq.	10-11 oz eq.
Dairy	2-3 c.	3 c.	3 c.	3 c.	3 c.	3 c.	3 c.	3 c.
Protein	4 oz eq.	5 oz eq.	5-5.5 oz eq.	5.5-6.5 oz eq.	6.5-7 oz eq.	7-7.5 oz eq.	7-7.5 oz eq.	7.5-8 oz eq.
Healthy Oils & Other Fats	4 tsp.	5 tsp.	5 tsp.	6 tsp.	6 tsp.	7 tsp.	8 tsp.	8 tsp.
Water & Super Beverages*	Women: 9 c. Men: 13 c.	Women: 9 c. Men: 13 c.	Women: 9 c. Men: 13 c.	Women: 9 c. Men: 13 c.	Women: 9 c. Men: 13 c.	Women: 9 c. Men: 13 c.	Women: 9 c. Men: 13 c.	Women: 9 c. Men: 13 c.

*May count up to 3 cups caffeinated tea or coffee toward goal

DAILY FOOD GROUP TRACKER

GROUP	FRUITS	VEGETABLES	GRAINS	PROTEIN	DAIRY	HEALTHY OILS & OTHER FATS	WATER & SUPER BEVERAGES
1 Estimate Total							
2 Estimate Total							
3 Estimate Total							
4 Estimate Total							
5 Estimate Total							
6 Estimate Total							
7 Estimate Total							

FOOD CHOICES   DAY ❶

Breakfast: _____
Lunch: _____
Dinner: _____
Snacks: _____

PHYSICAL ACTIVITY   steps/miles/minutes: _____

description: _____

SPIRITUAL ACTIVITY

description: _____

FOOD CHOICES   DAY ❷

Breakfast: ....
Lunch: ....
Dinner: ....
Snacks: ....

PHYSICAL ACTIVITY   steps/miles/minutes: | SPIRITUAL ACTIVITY

description: .... | description: ....

FOOD CHOICES   DAY ❸

Breakfast: ....
Lunch: ....
Dinner: ....
Snacks: ....

PHYSICAL ACTIVITY   steps/miles/minutes: | SPIRITUAL ACTIVITY

description: .... | description: ....

FOOD CHOICES   DAY ❹

Breakfast: ....
Lunch: ....
Dinner: ....
Snacks: ....

PHYSICAL ACTIVITY   steps/miles/minutes: | SPIRITUAL ACTIVITY

description: .... | description: ....

FOOD CHOICES   DAY ❺

Breakfast: ....
Lunch: ....
Dinner: ....
Snacks: ....

PHYSICAL ACTIVITY   steps/miles/minutes: | SPIRITUAL ACTIVITY

description: .... | description: ....

FOOD CHOICES   DAY ❻

Breakfast: ....
Lunch: ....
Dinner: ....
Snacks: ....

PHYSICAL ACTIVITY   steps/miles/minutes: | SPIRITUAL ACTIVITY

description: .... | description: ....

FOOD CHOICES   DAY ❼

Breakfast: ....
Lunch: ....
Dinner: ....
Snacks: ....

PHYSICAL ACTIVITY   steps/miles/minutes: | SPIRITUAL ACTIVITY

description: .... | description: ....

Name: _____

Date: _____ Week #: _____

My activity goal for next week:
○ None   ○ <30 min/day   ○ 30-60 min/day

loss / gain _____ Calorie Range: _____

My week at a glance:
○ Great   ○ So-so   ○ Not so great

My food goal for next week: _____

Activity level:
○ None   ○ <30 min/day   ○ 30-60 min/day

RECOMMENDED DAILY AMOUNT OF FOOD FROM EACH GROUP

GROUP	DAILY CALORIES							
	1300-1400	1500-1600	1700-1800	1900-2000	2100-2200	2300-2400	2500-2600	2700-2800
Fruits	1.5 – 2 c.	1.5 – 2 c.	1.5 – 2 c.	2 – 2.5 c.	2 – 2.5 c.	2.5 – 3.5 c.	3.5 – 4.5 c.	3.5 – 4.5 c.
Vegetables	1.5 – 2 c.	2 – 2.5 c.	2.5 – 3 c.	2.5 – 3 c.	3 – 3.5 c.	3.5 – 4.5 c.	4.5 – 5 c.	4.5 – 5 c.
Grains	5 oz eq.	5-6 oz eq.	6-7 oz eq.	6-7 oz eq.	7-8 oz eq.	8-9 oz eq.	9-10 oz eq.	10-11 oz eq.
Dairy	2-3 c.	3 c.	3 c.	3 c.	3 c.	3 c.	3 c.	3 c.
Protein	4 oz eq.	5 oz eq.	5-5.5 oz eq.	5.5-6.5 oz eq.	6.5-7 oz eq.	7-7.5 oz eq.	7-7.5 oz eq.	7.5-8 oz eq.
Healthy Oils & Other Fats	4 tsp.	5 tsp.	5 tsp.	6 tsp.	6 tsp.	7 tsp.	8 tsp.	8 tsp.
Water & Super Beverages*	Women: 9 c. Men: 13 c.	Women: 9 c. Men: 13 c.	Women: 9 c. Men: 13 c.	Women: 9 c. Men: 13 c.	Women: 9 c. Men: 13 c.	Women: 9 c. Men: 13 c.	Women: 9 c. Men: 13 c.	Women: 9 c. Men: 13 c.

*May count up to 3 cups caffeinated tea or coffee toward goal

DAILY FOOD GROUP TRACKER

GROUP	FRUITS	VEGETABLES	GRAINS	PROTEIN	DAIRY	HEALTHY OILS & OTHER FATS	WATER & SUPER BEVERAGES
1 Estimate Total							
2 Estimate Total							
3 Estimate Total							
4 Estimate Total							
5 Estimate Total							
6 Estimate Total							
7 Estimate Total							

FOOD CHOICES   **DAY 1**

Breakfast: _____

Lunch: _____

Dinner: _____

Snacks: _____

PHYSICAL ACTIVITY   steps/miles/minutes: _____

description: _____

SPIRITUAL ACTIVITY

description: _____

FOOD CHOICES · DAY ❷

Breakfast: _____
Lunch: _____
Dinner: _____
Snacks: _____

PHYSICAL ACTIVITY · steps/miles/minutes: _____
description: _____

SPIRITUAL ACTIVITY
description: _____

FOOD CHOICES · DAY ❸

Breakfast: _____
Lunch: _____
Dinner: _____
Snacks: _____

PHYSICAL ACTIVITY · steps/miles/minutes: _____
description: _____

SPIRITUAL ACTIVITY
description: _____

FOOD CHOICES · DAY ❹

Breakfast: _____
Lunch: _____
Dinner: _____
Snacks: _____

PHYSICAL ACTIVITY · steps/miles/minutes: _____
description: _____

SPIRITUAL ACTIVITY
description: _____

FOOD CHOICES · DAY ❺

Breakfast: _____
Lunch: _____
Dinner: _____
Snacks: _____

PHYSICAL ACTIVITY · steps/miles/minutes: _____
description: _____

SPIRITUAL ACTIVITY
description: _____

FOOD CHOICES · DAY ❻

Breakfast: _____
Lunch: _____
Dinner: _____
Snacks: _____

PHYSICAL ACTIVITY · steps/miles/minutes: _____
description: _____

SPIRITUAL ACTIVITY
description: _____

FOOD CHOICES · DAY ❼

Breakfast: _____
Lunch: _____
Dinner: _____
Snacks: _____

PHYSICAL ACTIVITY · steps/miles/minutes: _____
description: _____

SPIRITUAL ACTIVITY
description: _____

100-MILE CLUB

WALKING			
slowly, 2 mph	30 min =	156 cal =	1 mile
moderately, 3 mph	20 min =	156 cal =	1 mile
very briskly, 4 mph	15 min =	156 cal =	1 mile
speed walking	10 min =	156 cal =	1 mile
up stairs	13 min =	159 cal =	1 mile
RUNNING / JOGGING			
• • •	10 min =	156 cal =	1 mile
CYCLE OUTDOORS			
slowly, < 10 mph	20 min =	156 cal =	1 mile
light effort, 10-12 mph	12 min =	156 cal =	1 mile
moderate effort, 12-14 mph	10 min =	156 cal =	1 mile
vigorous effort, 14-16 mph	7.5 min =	156 cal =	1 mile
very fast, 16-19 mph	6.5 min =	152 cal =	1 mile
SPORTS ACTIVITIES			
playing tennis (singles)	10 min =	156 cal =	1 mile
swimming			
light to moderate effort	11 min =	152 cal =	1 mile
fast, vigorous effort	7.5 min =	156 cal =	1 mile
softball	15 min =	156 cal =	1 mile
golf	20 min =	156 cal =	1 mile
rollerblading	6.5 min =	152 cal =	1 mile
ice skating	11 min =	152 cal =	1 mile
jumping rope	7.5 min =	156 cal =	1 mile
basketball	12 min =	156 cal =	1 mile
soccer (casual)	15 min =	159 min =	1 mile
AROUND THE HOUSE			
mowing grass	22 min =	156 cal =	1 mile
mopping, sweeping, vacuuming	19.5 min =	155 cal =	1 mile
cooking	40 min =	160 cal =	1 mile
gardening	19 min =	156 cal =	1 mile
housework (general)	35 min =	156 cal =	1 mile

AROUND THE HOUSE			
ironing	45 min =	153 cal =	1 mile
raking leaves	25 min =	150 cal =	1 mile
washing car	23 min =	156 cal =	1 mile
washing dishes	45 min =	153 cal =	1 mile
AT THE GYM			
stair machine	8.5 min =	155 cal =	1 mile
stationary bike			
slowly, 10 mph	30 min =	156 cal =	1 mile
moderately, 10-13 mph	15 min =	156 cal =	1 mile
vigorously, 13-16 mph	7.5 min =	156 cal =	1 mile
briskly, 16-19 mph	6.5 min =	156 cal =	1 mile
elliptical trainer	12 min =	156 cal =	1 mile
weight machines (vigorously)	13 min =	152 cal =	1 mile
aerobics			
low impact	15 min =	156 cal =	1 mile
high impact	12 min =	156 cal =	1 mile
water	20 min =	156 cal =	1 mile
pilates	15 min =	156 cal =	1 mile
raquetball (casual)	15 min =	156 cal =	1 mile
stretching exercises	25 min =	150 cal =	1 mile
weight lifting (also works for weight machines used moderately or gently)	30 min =	156 cal =	1 mile
FAMILY LEISURE			
playing piano	37 min =	155 cal =	1 mile
jumping rope	10 min =	152 cal =	1 mile
skating (moderate)	20 min =	152 cal =	1 mile
swimming			
moderate	17 min =	156 cal =	1 mile
vigorous	10 min =	148 cal =	1 mile
table tennis	25 min =	150 cal =	1 mile
walk / run / play with kids	25 min =	150 cal =	1 mile

Let's Count Our Miles!

Color each circle to represent a mile you've completed.
Watch your progress to that 100 mile marker!

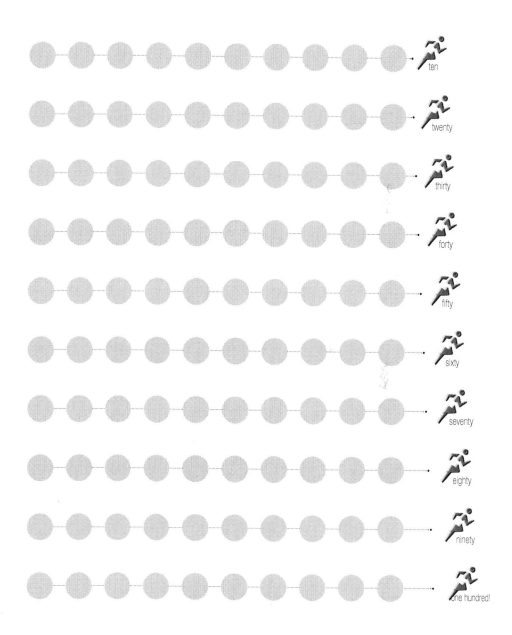

Made in the USA
Columbia, SC
24 March 2022